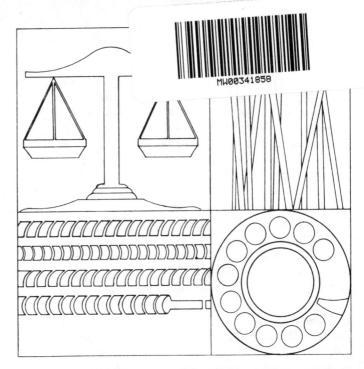

Commission Studies

Supporting
Materials
for the Report
of the

NATIONAL
COMMISSION
FOR THE REVIEW
OF FEDERAL
AND STATE LAWS
RELATING TO
WIRETAPPING AND
ELECTRONIC
SURVEILLANCE

WASHINGTON:
1976

Wiretapping and Electronic Surveillance

**Wiretapping and Electronic Surveillance
Commission Studies**

Published by:
Loompanics Unlimited
PO Box 1197
Pt. Townsend, WA 98368

Preface

The development of semiconductor technology, (in 1954), revolutionized the science of electronics by affording a limitless range of miniaturization capabilities. While the benefits of "solid-state" electronics have greatly exceeded the expectations of its originators, the discovery has opened a Pandora's Box from which has emerged a fascinating variety of Big Brother hardware, some of which exceeds the fantasies of Orwell.

Inspired by the phenomenal marketing success of the "pocket-size" radio, infant foreign industries began producing inexpensive, "little black box" devices, millions of which were imported to the U.S. and sold openly in electronics specialty shops. Thus the era of anybody-can-do-it electronic surveillance was born and conventional notions about privacy began to fade. The birth of this apparent menace to privacy and "secret dealings" generated a wave of paranoia, affecting mainly those who have most to fear. The reaction in Washington was rather like the discovery of peepholes in a convent shower-room, thus, in the interest of protecting the average citizen, (naturally), a special session of The Congress convened to draft a law, (Public Law 90-351), that made the offense of performing electronic surveillance as serious as forcible rape for anybody other than "authorized" policemen, (of course).

Because the subject matter of the new taboo was substantially technical, and politicians have little awareness of such mundane things, a special commission was appointed by the President to prepare an official report. The report took approximately two years to compile, drawing on the efforts of numerous experts, including engineers, countermeasures specialists, and the like. It was presented to President Gerald Ford on April 30, 1976, in the form of a 240 page document, entitled, *Commission Studies*.

This document has earned some measure of historical significance in that it was commissioned by the government and represents the collective knowledge of a select group of experts on a specific activity which has become anathema and worthy of severe federal punishment.

The first 140 pages of the *Commission Studies* report is dull and typically bureaucratic, consisting of analyses of the new laws and citing similar circumstances in foreign countries. However, the second and third sections of *Commission Studies*, (entitled "State of the Art of Electronic Surveillance," and "The Authentication of Magnetic Tapes"), are veritable gold-mines of practical information relating to the nuts & bolts of wiretapping and bugging! They contain surprisingly thorough, illustrated descriptions of a wide variety of electronic surveillance techniques and devices.

The following pages are an exact, unedited reproduction of the *State of the Art of Electronic Surveillance* and *The Authentication of Magnetic Tapes*, extracted directly from a copy of the original *Commission Studies* report as it was presented to President Ford on April 30, 1976.

Michael Kessler
May 25, 1983

Contents

State of the Art of Electronic Surveillance

List of Illustrations

List of Tables

The Authentication of Magnetic Tapes

List of Illustrations

STATE OF THE ART OF ELECTRONIC SURVEILLANCE

Prepared by John S. VanDewerker, Ashby & Associates.

Ashby & Associates was formed in November 1968. In October 1971, its Systems Division was formed for the purpose of providing electronic security countermeasure products and technical services. After serving on a part-time basis with the Systems Division from 1971 to 1974, John S. VanDewerker became the general manager of that division in 1974. Mr. VanDewerker holds a BSEE from Washington State University, and completed graduate work in control systems at George Washington University. From 1967 to 1974, he was employed by the Central Intelligence Agency as a Program Evaluation Officer.

ABSTRACT

The Science of Electronic Surveillance

This document presents the results of an extensive data gathering and analysis effort, organized and completed over a seven month period, and addresses each of the following five areas:

1.0—Eavesdropping Equipment—This Section includes a review of telephone eavesdropping devices, radio transmitters, passive and active listening devices, audio system accessories, and sophisticated eavesdropping techniques.

2.0—Countermeasures Equipment—This Section discusses counter-surveillance radio receivers, telephone analysis equipment, electronic aids to physical inspection, and protection devices such as acoustic rooms, disconnect devices, filters, and various radio jammers.

3.0—Penetration of Other Information Handling Systems—This Section addresses computer security and eavesdropping on information processing machines.

4.0—Electronic Aids to Physical Surveillance—This Section reviews night viewing devices and systems, and various tracking devices such as beacons and radio navigation systems.

5.0—Systems of the Future—This Section projects the development of surveillance technologies into systems which may become available in the foreseeable future. These include various devices for signal and voice processing, radio modulation and transmission, electo-optical imaging, and information recording.

As an aid to the non-technical reader, a brief tutorial defines basic terminology and scientific principles that allow understanding of eavesdropping devices and practices. This electronics primer is enhanced by a glossary of terms to guide the reader through the text.

As a summary of the extensive presentation regarding equipment characteristics and capabilities, a series of findings ascertained during this study are presented. Conclusions drawn from these numerous findings are presented as are several recommendations that effect a purpose for the completion and documentation of this work.

ACKNOWLEDGEMENTS

The authors wish to express appreciation to the following individuals for their assistance, recommendations, and contributions made during the course of this study and their worthwhile opinions which were frequently solicited:

Mrs. Sybil S. Barefoot

Mr. Glenn A. Burklund

Mr. Charles E. Gaskin.

Commission Staff Note: The Commission's Request for a Proposal for a Study of the State of the Art of Electronic Surveillance advised contractors to include consideration of the following subjects and items:

1. Today's commercially available equipment for voice interception: kinds, basic characteristics, effectiveness, costs, and frequency of use. (Federally classified information is excluded.) Electronic components and their potential for use in assembling illegal devices should be explored.

2. Countermeasures: Examples, capability, cost, effectiveness. What is envisioned is a rather brief commentary on countermeasure equipment, its use, and effectiveness with respect to the kinds of commercially available equipment discussed in item 1, above.

3. Other kinds of communications which are subject to interception: transmission of data from computer to computer, pen registers, telephone decoders, etc.

4. Aids to physical surveillance: video cameras and "bumper beepers," etc.

5. Today's technology and its impact on tomorrow's threat to the invasion of privacy: the practical application of science to electronic surveillance in the forseeable future, to include consideration of such matters as miniaturization, integrated circuits, laser, radar, infra red, X-rays, voice prints, optical fiber (integrated optics), and higher frequency transmission.

REVIEW OF TERMINOLOGY

A comprehensive discussion of the state of the art in any technology requires that the reader be familiar with the basic concepts of that technology so that full appreciation of the information presented is possible. So it is with this report wherein, not only an understanding of the basic electronic and physical concepts is required, but also an understanding of the practice of audio surveillance is necessary. Uncertainty with these concepts can cause ambiguities in the reader's mind, which reduce appreciation for the characteristics and operational capability of specific electronic surveillance tools.

It is the intent of this introductory section to familiarize the reader with the technical concepts that are used repeatedly in the text and bring a level of understanding sufficient for obtaining full benefit from the discussion. This introduction, when reviewed in conjunction with the Glossary, should provide a basic understanding of the technical concepts of: frequency, electrical energy, magnetism, and modulation, and their place in the world of electronic surveillance.

Frequency

Frequency is one of many terms used to describe a characteristic common to microphones, radio transmitters, surveillance receivers and even laser light beams. It refers to the number of times a cyclical motion such as a vibration is repeated in a specific time interval. If the time interval is equal to one second, the frequency is the total number of times per second the repetitive incident occurs and is referred to as Hertz and is abbreviated Hz. This term is named in honor of the German physicist Heinrich Rudolf Hertz, 1857-94, who discovered radio waves. For example, a room fan which revolves ten times in one second has a frequency of 10 Hz; human speech generated by the vibrating vocal cords consists of audible sounds with frequencies generally in the range of 90 Hz to above 7,000 Hz. A range of frequencies is referred to as a spectrum or frequency band. In this case, human speech has a spectrum on the order of 90 Hz to above 7,000 Hz.

The concept of frequency is consistent regardless of the particular surveillance device being described. As frequencies increase they occur higher in the total spectrum of frequencies; above those of human speech are radio broadcasts, television and light. The complete frequency spectrum is illustrated in Figure 1.

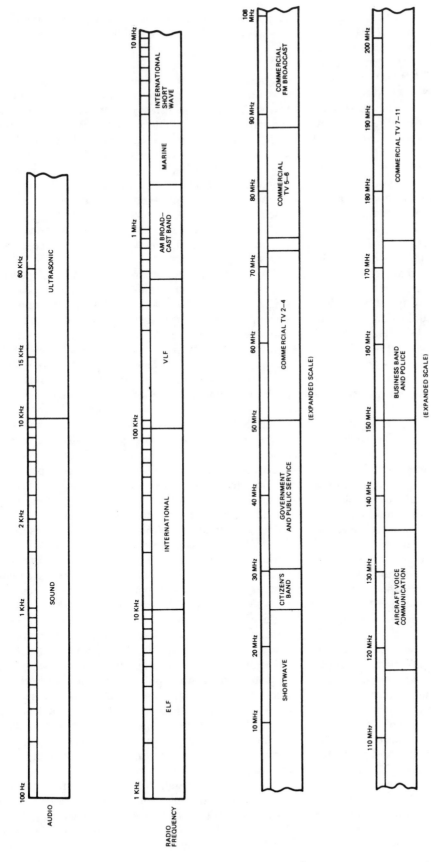

FIGURE I. FREQUENCY SPECTRUM CHART

3

In the radio frequency range of 550 thousand to 1,600 thousand Hz (Kilo Hertz [KHz] for thousands of cycles per second) is the commercial AM radio broadcast portion of the spectrum. At 88 MHz to 108 MHz (one thousand KHz is one million cycles per second and is known as Mega Hertz [MHz]) is the standard FM commercial broadcast band. The terms Kilo (thousands) Hz and Mega (millions) Hz refer to the number of times per second the radio energy is varying and these abbreviated terms are much easier to use in discussions of electrical characteristics than thousands and millions of cycles. Above the commercial radio broadcast frequencies are frequency regions known as Very High Frequency (VHF) and Ultra High Frequency (UHF). Most commercial radio eavesdropping devices operate at frequencies in these regions. Figure 1 also illustrates the many channels or radio frequencies allocated by the Federal Communications Commission (FCC) for a specific use. For example, aircraft voice communications use the frequency spectrum between 118 MHz and 138 MHz; police use frequencies between 150 MHz and 160 MHz.

Frequency specification is critical to the description of eavesdropping radio transmitters and receivers because it immediately identifies where in the spectrum the transmitter emits its signal and likewise where the receiver must be tuned to receive it. Because of this allocation of frequencies and the need to have a companion receiver with each transmitter, many eavesdropping transmitters operate in or near the commercial broadcast portions of the spectrum because easily modified, inexpensive portable radio receivers can be used to receive these signals. In the eavesdropping business operating frequencies are carefully selected to prevent casual or accidental detection, but the price paid for increased freedom from detection may be high. In general, as transmission frequency increases so does the cost of both the transmitter and receiver.

Other performance characteristics controlled by transmission frequency are the effective transmission range, susceptibility to static or other electrical noises, and ability to pass through or around large physical objects such as hills or buildings. These latter characteristics become more acute as frequency increases to the point where the radio signal will travel only in a straight line and pass very poorly through or around solid objects.

Understanding the concepts of frequency and spectrum is important to understanding the advantages or limitations of a specific surveillance device. In many cases frequency may be the only technical difference between devices and be the major determining characteristic which controls cost, performance, and capability.

Energy

Energy is a term used to describe an ability to perform work; the greater the energy, the greater is this ability to work. Energy identifies one aspect of the capability of a material or device, such as the energy contained in a gallon of gasoline, the sun's solar energy which can heat a home, or the stored energy in a lake behind a dam which can be converted to electrical energy and routed over wires to a consumer. In this report, electrical energy is discussed from several viewpoints including electrical voltage, electrical current, and electrical resistance, since each affects the performance of an eavesdropping device.

To develop an appreciation for these electrical terms, consider the analogy of a water pipe and spigot in a conventional household plumbing system. In this comparison, the water pressure is equivalent to electrical voltage and water flow equivalent to electrical current. If the spigot is closed, the pressure behind the spigot exists within the pipe; if the spigot is opened, water will flow out depending on the size of the opening and the amount of pressure. In this case the flow of water is controlled by the pressure in the pipe and the size of the opening which offers some resistance to the flow. In an electrical equivalent, when a power source such as a battery exerts a voltage pressure on an electronic device, the amount of current which flows depends on the resistance offered by the device and the capacity of the battery.

In the normal household, the voltage pressure is 110 to 120 volts and the electrical flow of current is limited by a fuse in the fuse-box or circuit breaker to about 20 amperes. Volts are the measurement units for voltage and amperes are the measurement units for current. The simple "D" size flashlight battery has a voltage of only 1.5 volts and a current flow cabability of approximately one-half ampere. It is important to note here that the physical size of a battery does not change the voltage available, only its capacity to supply a large flow of current. These two electrical characteristics of voltage and current, when multiplied, result in the total power consumed by an electronic device and is expressed in watts. For example, in the case of the flashlight battery, if 1.5 volts is multiplied by 0.5 amperes the resulting power is 0.75 watts.

All batteries supply direct current meaning that neither the current nor voltage varies regularly with time, but household current does vary at a fixed frequency of 60 Hz. In the home a 150 watt lightbulb operating from a 110 to 120 volt AC (alternating current) circuit would draw approximately 1.4 amperes of electrical current. A lightbulb with a higher power rating, such as 500 watts, would consume more current but illuminate a larger area. The concept of power in a surveillance device connotes that greater power provides greater operating range at the same frequency. Unlike lightbulbs, most eavesdropping devices consume and radiate only 1/100th to 1/10,000th the power available from household electrical wiring. For these reasons, the terms milliwatt (mw), meaning 1-1000th of a watt, millivolt (mv), meaning 1-1000th of a volt, and a milliampere (ma), meaning 1-1000th of an ampere, were formed to permit easy expression of these smaller units of electrical characteristics.

Throughout the technical discussion of this report, the term milliwatt is occasionally used to specify the power of a surveillance device. It is the basic electrical characteristic which can usually be related to the effective operating range of a surveillance transmitter. In the electronic surveillance area, amounts of power are generally small and the usual clandestine transmitter is rated at ten to twenty milliwatts, which, depending on frequency and other physical factors, may have a range of one to six city blocks. Higher powered body transmitters may produce 100 milliwatts to 1 watt and beacon tracking transmitters 1 to 2 watts. The ranges associated with the higher powered devices are usually in excess of 6 blocks and could be several miles under favorable conditions.

The effect of power consumption on battery life is of great importance. A device consuming ten milliwatts which operates for ten hours from one battery of a specific size, may operate one-half as long from a battery of one-half the capacity and conversely, doubling the battery capacity may double the transmitter operating life. Increasing the voltage does tend to increase the power output of the device and thus increases the effective operating range. This latter technique is common practice for a user of the so-called wireless microphone where a single battery is replaced by two batteries in series which increases the effective range of this transmitter.

Magnetism

Magnetism is recognized in its steady, unvarying state as that force which is present in a simple permanent magnet. If, however, the physical position of this force is changed while in the vicinity of a length of wire, an electrical current will flow through this wire. By exploiting this electrical phenomena, several beneficial things can be made to happen including the generation of electrical power and the conversion of audio sound into electrical signals. Any changing or moving magnetic field will induce a current flow in a piece of wire and conversely, any current flowing through a piece of wire will create a proportional magnetic field. This reciprocal relationship between electrical current and magnetism is a key factor in the technical performance of several basic eavesdropping devices. One device commonly used in conducting electronic surveillance is the magnetic microphone which converts audio sound vibrations into electrical signals by vibrating a coil of fine wires in a magnetic field as shown in Figure 2. Another is the sensing of a magnetic field which surrounds the telephone instrument and transmission wires with a small coil of wire or induction coil as shown in Figure 4. Here, the changing magnetic field induces or generates a proportional electrical signal in the coil. Even the eavesdropper's earphones, Figure 3, behave in this same predictable manner; the electrical signal flowing through a coil of wire generates a magnetic field which moves a thin metal plate or diaphragm at an audio frequency rate which in turn vibrates the air creating sound that can be heard by the human ear.

5

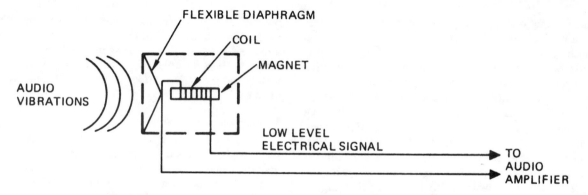

ELECTRICAL SIGNAL GENERATED BY COIL MOVEMENT AROUND MAGNET
IS PROPORTIONAL TO AUDIO VIBRATIONS PRESENT AT DIAPHRAGM

FIGURE 2. MAGNETIC MICROPHONE

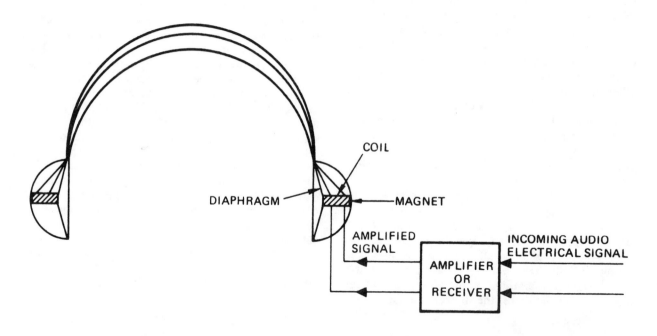

AMPLIFIED ELECTRICAL SIGNAL APPLIED TO COIL CREATES DIAPHRAGM
MOVEMENT. DIAPHRAGM MOVEMENT REPRODUCES INCOMING ELECTRICAL
SIGNAL AS AN AUDIO SIGNAL

FIGURE 3. MAGNETIC EARPHONE

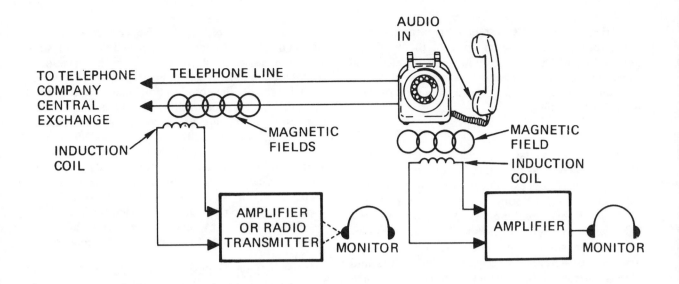

MAGNETIC FIELD SURROUNDING TELEPHONE WIRE AND INSTRUMENT IS PROPORTIONAL TO THE AUDIO SIGNAL

INDUCTION COIL TRANSFORMS MAGNETIC FIELD VARIATIONS TO AN ELECTRICAL SIGNAL

LOW LEVEL ELECTRICAL SIGNALS ARE AMPLIFIED FOR AUDIO MONITORING OR RADIO TRANSMISSION

FIGURE 4. INDUCTIVE SENSING

In the context of this report, measurement of magnetism is not necessary because the basic understanding of this relationship between electrical signals and magnetic or inductive forces is all that is required to appreciate the significance of many surveillance techniques.

Modulation

The term "modulation" means to momentarily change or vary with time some normally unvarying and continuous process. These brief variations correspond directly to some desired message. In a crude sense this would include turning on and off a light switch in a series of dots and dashes to modulate the intensity or amplitude of light energy from a lamp. Furthermore, if groups of these dots and dashes correspond to alphabetic letters, as in Morse Code, a message is contained in this modulated light. This modulation is known as digital, pulse, or on-off keying and is similar to that used by teletypewriters or computer terminals. If this light switch were replaced by a dimmer type control, the lamp could be turned up and down to vary the light intensity without completely turning it on and off. If this intensity is varied rapidly and continuously, corresponding to the frequencies contained in human speech, then the amplitude of the light is being modulated in an analogue fashion rather than a digital or pulse mode.

In radio communications the amplitude of a single radio frequency, perhaps 100 MHz, could be switched on and off or varied continuously in the same manner as the light and likewise carry the same message. In this case the radio signal could carry the message over a considerable distance. This is Amplitude Modulation (AM), one of the earliest forms of modulation and is still used today in the commercial AM broadcast band.

Since the process of modulation means momentarily varying any stable characteristic of a signal, such as the amplitude or intensity of the signal, other continuous characteristics may also be varied or modulated. Again, consider the single frequency radio signal operating continuously at 100 MHz. Rather than momentarily turning the signal off and on and thereby change its amplitude, slightly change the frequency. Now, rather than operating at exactly 100 MHz, the radio signal frequency might be varied at an audio rate about the central frequency of 100 MHz. If this process is repeated corresponding to a desired message, then the radio signal is being frequency modulated (FM) rather than amplitude modulated (AM) as described in the earlier example of the on/off light switching or intensity variation.

These modulations are known conventionally as FM and AM and each is one specification of surveillance device performance, since the reception or detection of these devices requires specific knowledge of the modulation being used. The eavesdropper, by controlling the type of modulation used in a clandestine device, may incorporate additional privacy and freedom from discovery since the choice of modulations are numerous. In some cases a single radio frequency could be modulated a number of times to prevent accidental detection. In a sense, knowing the modulation technique chosen for use in an electronic surveillance device is a key factor to receiving the radio signal and being able to decode, that is, understand the message.

When a single radio frequency carrier is modulated by an audio signal that contains frequencies of 3000 Hz, the single carrier frequency will vary over a limited excursion about this single frequency. This excursion is known as the "bandwidth" of the radio signal. If a radio receiver is tuned to the radio carrier frequency, it must have at least the same bandwidth capability to receive and process the 3000 Hz audio signal. The concept of bandwidth is important in specifying the performance and capability of a receiver or radio detection device, for if the receiver does not have the necessary bandwidth, it will not receive and effectively demodulate the signal.

INTRODUCTION

The reasonable expectation of privacy is an individual's right guaranteed within the broad legal framework of our open society. This guarantee, however, has become increasingly difficult to ensure because of the advent of surreptitious electronic devices which are now found throughout this country. The public was basically unprotected from technically inspired invasion of privacy until 1968 when the Omnibus Crime Control and Safe Streets Act became law. Title III of that Act was designed to protect each American's privacy from intrusion by the mechanisms of electronic surveillance, except under certain limited and specifically prescribed circumstances recognized by the U.S. Supreme Court as being constitutionally permissible.

This legislative effort to control surveillance has been tested for over six years. Rapid advances in electronic technology have opened new avenues for surveillance techniques; some are extremely complex, such as the "laser window pickoff", and some are deceivingly simple, such as the "telephone compromise". For the most part, the technology application is easily within the capabilities of the electronic technician and hobbyist. To this readily evident environment may be added the conjunctive conditions of improved technical communications, cross fertilization of ideas by electronic engineers which is enhanced by job mobility, and increased availability and reduced costs of components which arise with the enhanced productivity of the blossoming electronics industry. Congress exercised remarkable foresight in mandating by statute that a National Commission would review the first six years of experience under this law and would report to the President and the Congress whether any changes should be made.

OBJECTIVE

The purpose for conducting this study is to assist the National Wiretap Commission in defining the characteristics, effectiveness, use, and cost of electronic eavesdropping devices and other technically facilitated invasions of privacy by establishing the current state of the art in surveillance technologies. It is intended to be a thorough review and summary that is descriptive of devices used by public law enforcement organizations and by the domestic sector in private and industrial surveillance activities. This overview is a summary of equipment characteristics including voice communications gathering effectiveness, frequency of use, and device costs. Also included within the scope of this document is a review of other electronic aids for information gathering and individual surveillance. These include computer data intercept techniques, vehicle and cargo tracking systems, and low light level imagery or night viewing visual aids. To provide the Commission and the public with a realistic perspective of electronic privacy invasion, the report also presents a critical review of those defensive electronic countermeasures devices and services which are available for those who seriously believe that their privacy is being threatened.

Since the objective of this Commission is to review the effectiveness of legislation enacted in 1968 and offer constructive criticism in the form of recommendations for modifying legislation, a liberal amount of forward thinking is necessary. Therefore, the reasonable projection of futuristic electronic threats is of importance for an effective definition of recommendations that are anticipatory of tomorrow's needs. This projection is one principal goal of this study.

METHODOLOGY

Information for this report was gathered and substantiated by completing four basic tasks. These included:

a. Interviews with over 18 select members of the law enforcement, federal, and industrial communities familiar with the surveillance technologies;
b. Survey of 120 law enforcement organizations determining surveillance device type, inventory, frequency and practices of use;
c. Collection and review of over 200 equipment catalogues in the audio, visual, and physical surveillance fields; and
d. Identification and assembly of over 180 published journal articles, books, advertisements and government reports.

Data gathered from these sources were subject to critical review and analysis to determine their relevance to this study and to insure its technical integrity.

SUMMARY OF FINDINGS

This summary presents the principal findings determined as a result of this study and subsequent analysis. Findings are grouped according to subject areas. The numerous devices that are distributed into these five areas are the focal point of examination in this study, and are discussed in detail in another section in this report.

Audio Eavesdropping

Findings in this area are divided among: telephone system surveillance, microphones, radio transmitters, optical transmitters and recording devices.

Telephone System Surveillance. Various audio eavesdropping devices use or exploit the telephone system in two distinct ways: those which intercept actual telephone conversations; and those which use parts of the system to facilitate room eavesdropping. Use of some devices requires access to the target area or instrument prior to eavesdropping, while other techniques do not necessitate entry to the premises to implement the eavesdropping.

The interception of normal telephone conversations, or wiretapping, is conducted either by connecting a listening device directly to the lines (hardwire tap) to by attachment of a radio transmitter. All parts required to complete a hardwire tap are available to the private sector without restriction because, individually, each component is not identifiable as an audio eavesdropping device. The devices used for successful radio tapping of the telephone, however, are not readily available because of their apparent eavesdropping nature and are more costly and usually less reliable in use than those required for hardwire tapping. For these reasons, and for its superior security, the hardwire tap is the more frequently used technique among law enforcement organizations.

Portions of the normal telephone system may be manipulated or modified and made to serve as part of the audio eavesdropping system. One device that uses part of the telephone system, the infinity transmitter, performs well as a room bug and is offered for sale to the public as a burglar alarm.

Room eavesdropping is also possible with a modified telephone instrument, where the handset serves as the microphone, and the modified instrument uses additional electronic parts which are inexpensive and readily available in most radio-TV and electronic retail stores. The use of this latter technique is limited, however, because of the technical skill and expertise required to modify the telephone instrument.

Microphones. Recent developments in microphone technology, due in part to growth of the commercial tape recorder and hearing aid market, have resulted in abundant supply of very small microphones. Singularly, microphones do not constitute an electronic eavesdropping threat because additional components are required to make a complete surveillance device. The procedure of room eavesdropping by use of a small microphone and wire system, although most reliable and virtually undetectable, remains unattractive to eavesdroppers because of the difficult installation problem and the technical expertise needed to assure proper operation.

Radio Transmitters. Radio transmitters used for eavesdropping are generally restricted to those devices small enough for easy concealment. Three groups of transmitters were found to satisfy this criterion, each identifiable by relative differences in cost, sophistication, and availability.

The least costly, most available, and widely used devices in the private sector are identified as baby monitors or wireless microphones in mail order or magazine advertisements. These devices were found to be in most frequent use, since they require little, if any, modification, are difficult to trace to the user of the device, are inexpensive, and require an inexpensive portable radio normally used for commercial broadcast reception. Their principal limitations are short range, poor reliability, and high probability of accidental detection, since they usually operate directly in or near the commercial FM broadcast radio frequency band.

The second category of transmitters are those inexpensive devices not readily identifiable as surveillance devices and which require modification by the eavesdropper for conversion to a surveillance device. Within this group are inexpensive walkie-talkies, or two-way radios, used in citizen band and amateur radio equipment.

The sophisticated group of transmitters includes those used by law enforcement. These tend to be more effective, smaller, and more secure for surveillance applications. These are frequently offered for sale preconcealed in various household fixtures such as ashtrays, picture frames and lamps.

Optical Systems. Audio eavesdropping systems exist which operate by using either visible or nonvisible light beam transmissions to carry audio information. These systems function either as a communications link between a planted surveillance device and the listening post or as an illuminating beam of light energy that retrieves audio vibrations from a target area by bouncing the light from a vibrating, reflective surface such as a window.

The use of light beams for point-to-point communications is fairly common in industry. Equipment, both transmitters and receivers, although expensive, are commercially available. A very attractive feature of an optical eavesdropping link is the low probability of detection during use. This feature, however, is offset by difficult installation and operational problems and this technique is relatively unattractive for the eavesdropper.

The use of laser beams to retrieve audio from vibrating window panes, although highly publicized, was not found to exist outside the experimental laboratory. This technology offers no substantive threat at the present time because of the high cost of special equipment, restrictive physical considerations, and skill required for successful operation.

Recording Devices. A number of recording systems were identified which allow operating times of up to eight hours and a few with recording durations of twenty-four hours without the need to change recording tape. Each was a component of a recording system designed for use by the police, telephone companies, airlines, or the entertainment industry. They were not found to be attractive as a part of a surreptitious audio eavesdropping system, mainly because of size and cost.

Standard cassette recorders were frequently found coupled with voice actuation switching devices designed to extend their operating time and provide unmanned operation. Typically, these systems were prepackaged in standard briefcases and controlled by concealed switches. The microphone is usually hidden behind the briefcase clasp, lock, or hinge and installed to ensure good performance while the briefcase is closed. These nominally priced systems were not found to be readily available to the private sector because of their obvious audio eavesdropping capabilities. Several complete briefcase units were found which contained not only voice actuated recorders but also radio receivers that permit automatic recording of signals received from a remote, companion radio transmitter.

Recording system miniaturization technology has provided the audio surveillance practitioner with small units having operating times of approximately one hour. One, the size of a cigarette lighter, operates for several hours but is quite expensive and available only through European outlets. Slightly larger but less costly devices have become quite popular for short term recordings and are used in a consensual environment.

Countermeasures

Audio countermeasures is the term used to describe the encompassing practice of detecting audio eavesdropping devices or protection from the effects of these devices. It requires both a skilled technician and sophisticated electronic equipment and is commonly termed "debugging".

Findings fall into four categories: telephone systems, microphones, radio transmitters, and service organizations.

Telephone Systems. No countermeasures equipment was found which could conclusively determine the existence of a properly installed wiretap. Furthermore, it was determined that only close visual inspection of the entire telephone line could resolve this question.

Several companies offer electronic telephone instrument analysis equipment which, if properly operated, could determine the existence of a tone activated infinity transmitter as well as numerous types of telephone instrument modifications.

A limited number of suppliers were found which offer systems designed to protect the individual from eavesdropping resulting from telephone modifications. These equipments include switching devices to isolate the unused telephone from the external telephone wires and jamming devices that inject noise into the instrument or telephone lines to make them unuseable for eavesdropping.

Microphone and Wire Systems. No countermeasures equipments were found that reliably locate microphones. Metal detectors may locate a microphone, if it is installed in an area where no other metal objects exist and the detector passes in close proximity to the microphone.

Radio Transmitters. Radio transmitters used for surveillance can be located in many ways with equipment offered by many manufacturers. These detection units were found to exist in three generic categories: radio signal energy measuring devices (field strength meters or "sniffers"), radio frequency analyzers (spectrum analyzers), and counter-

measures radio receivers or combinations of these equipments. If the eavesdropping transmitter is active and transmitting a radio signal, any of the aforementioned detectors may determine its presence. In general, for any given situation the performance of the radio signal energy measurement device is inferior to both the analyzer and countermeasures receiver. The latter two are frequently used together to provide the operator an increased analytical capability.

Service Organizations. Few commercial organizations were found that were able to demonstrate extensive competence in performing the services of audio countermeasures device design, facilities technical inspection, protection from surveillance invasions, or consulting services. Six firms were found that appeared to have sufficient electronic countermeasures equipment and professionally trained, experienced personnel to perform this service. Unfortunately, in the private sector it is difficult to identify competent countermeasures organizations. While it is legal to advertise countermeasures services, the media is reluctant, by policy, to accept such advertising because of fears regarding misrepresentations by the advertiser. Further, no licensing procedures or standards exist by which service organizations are evaluated and by which evaluations are made known to the public.

Interception of Non-Audio Information

Intercepting non-audio information means intercepting those communications which are not human speech. Specifically, this includes teletype and bulk or multi-channel data communication transmissions, computer data, and information processing machine emanations. These types of interceptions are not addressed in Title III of the Omnibus Crime and Safe Streets Act of 1968, which defines an intercept as the "aural" acquisition of a wire or oral communication.

Bulk Data Communication Links. Radio receiving equipment was found to exist and is publicly available that permits the interception of communications channels. After signal reception by the eavesdropper, however, signal processing is required to reconstruct the audio information. This technical imposition removes this practice from most conventional eavesdropper's capability. This information gathering activity was found to be of interest principally to federal organizations and some large corporations.

Computer Systems. This area was found to be by far the most active in non-audio eavesdropping. Interception and manipulation of data occurs between a time-shared computer subscriber remote terminal (such as at banks, credit bureaus, or secu-

11

rities brokers) and the central computer. Signal reception can be implemented through the use of standard audio eavesdropping devices and is difficult to trace. Interpretation and control of the digital data signals requires the use of a modestly expensive computer keyboard terminal and in some cases a mini-computer. The technical skills required are moderate but the rewards for the eavesdropper may be considerable, and therefore, quite attractive to the skilled, professional criminal. Awareness of this interception activity has caused industry to increase computer security, a difficult task in view of the diversified talents of private sector computer eavesdroppers.

Electronic Aids to Physical Surveillance

It was found that extensive electronic assistance is available to law enforcement and security organizations for night viewing and vehicle or cargo tracking. The market for these aids was found to be much greater than for audio eavesdropping devices. All devices available are apparently legal as none of these items are considered to be eavesdropping devices. The devices only assist human senses and have an established position in the physical security field. A brief statement of findings is made below.

Visual Systems. Several manufacturers offer small, hand-held, light amplifying or illuminating devices which permit the detection of a human being at one thousand feet and identification at approximately one-fifth that distance under very low light level conditions. All systems were found to vary greatly in size, cost, capability, and application, ranging from direct viewing pistol grip devices to night observation devices with large lens extensions. All devices and systems were found to be expensive and some systems afford photographic or video capability.

Tracking Systems. Most vehicle and cargo tracking systems found to be used by law enforcement agencies consist of a beacon transmitting device and a companion receiving device to detect these signals. Tracking systems vary in quality depending upon the amount of radio signal processing done to determine range and direction of the beacon from the receiver. Generally, most systems provide a left-right meter indication of direction and a relative range estimate to the operator. Each system was found to be moderately expensive. Use of tracking systems varies greatly among organizations because of the level of operator skill required for successful operation. Most systems were capable of operation from both aircraft and automobiles with the superior performance being experienced with the former.

Several newer technologies were identified which allow simultaneous tracking of many vehicles from a single control station. These systems are not uniquely applicable to covert law enforcement tracking operations; however, due to the high capital investment, size, and complexity, such systems were found to be intended for civil use in traffic and mass transit systems management.

Systems of the Future

There is minimal value in assessing the current status of electronic eavedropping systems for the purpose of conceiving legislation intended to be effective in the future. A projection of these eavesdropping technologies was made in the areas of communications systems, microphones, and recorders, since each is critical to future capabilities of electronic privacy intrusion devices. Future technology, in general, is developing from the advancement of commercial industries.

Communications. New developments in the telecommunications industry were found and others are expected that will make surveillance more difficult for the electronic eavesdropper. This is primarily due to anticipated telephone and visual system developments, including optical fibers which carry light energy, and special high frequency radio signals which are conducted inside buried, metal pipes. These developments are being stimulated by the need for larger capacity communications systems and not by improved security needs. Because of the technical complexities involved, it can be surmised that eavesdroppers of tomorrow will be faced with a very complex problem; however, judging from past performance and the technical ingenuity displayed by the eavesdropper, it may be expected that any communications system of the future could be compromised.

Radio Transmitters and Receivers. The current physical size of radio transmitters and receivers used in electronic surveillance will undoubtedly diminish, but this may be of limited benefit if battery technology does not progress at a similar rate. If not, the size of an easily concealable listening device will be limited by its battery power supply.

It has been found that an emerging technology may partially solve this size problem. New microcomputer processor techniques of the type provided in pocket calculators are being used in the development of a significant new radio signal processing capability.

Microphones. Reducing microphone size would be of little significance because it is not a limiting factor in the size of future eavesdropping devices. Improvements in microphone performance, however, and in microcomputer audio processing and noise filtering techniques will lead to improvements in audio surveillance device capability.

Recorders. Both the performance and size characteristics of recorders can be expected to improve in the future due to advances in audio processing, mechanical design, and recording tape materials. It has been found that signal processing technology, again supported by microcomputers, can condense human speech to store more information in a given length of recording tape. Improvements in mechanical design should permit size reduction and more precise control of the recording tape drive mechanism; and common, magnetic plastic tape should become narrower, thinner, and stronger. Cumulatively, these advances will bring about recording devices which are much smaller than today's cigarette package size eavesdrooping radio transmitters and will operate for several hours or days with built-in voice control actuators. Because of this impending decreased size, recording devices may be used in lieu of body transmitters except in those situations where continuous communication with others is essential.

CONCLUSIONS

Based on the stated findings, the following conclusions were drawn with regard to the present level of eavesdropping activity, the availability of supportive electronic devices, and the current legal structure.

Audio Eavesdropping Devices

Telephone Systems. It is concluded that:

1. It would be very difficult to control the practice of wiretapping by controlling the availability of equipment employed in the procedure since not all are uniquely identifiable as eavesdropping devices.

2. It would be virtually impossible to control the availability of those standard electronic parts which can be installed within the telephone instrument to convert it into a room eavesdropping device.

3. It may be possible to control the availability of inexpensive audio burglar alarm devices which can be used for room eavesdropping without modification.

Microphones. It is concluded that no control over the availability of microphones is necessary because of their fundamental position as a component in a vast, commercial market.

Radio Transmitters. It is concluded that:

1. The availability of inexpensive radio transmitters offered to the public under the guise of wireless microphones can be constrained without undue, adverse effects on the private sector.

2. Control over the availability of industrial communications and amateur radio equipment is un-

necessary and undesirable, but that consideration of methods to prevent equipment modification for eavesdropping purposes warrants study.

3. No controls exist over the publication of instructions, schematics, or diagrams relative to fabrication of radio eavesdropping devices.

4. Better public knowledge and legal definition is necessary to improve practices of manufacturing, marketing, and advertising of radio transmitters.

Optical Systems. It is concluded that control is unnecessary and undesirable over optical equipment availability because of the wide commercial use of laser and other light beam devices.

Recording Devices. It is concluded that no further control is necessary or desirable regarding the availability of conventional recording equipment.

Countermeasures

Based upon observations made during this study and the data reviewed in the countermeasures product and service area, it is concluded that:

1. Equipment performance claims by manufacturers are often ambiguous or frequently misleading to both the technical and non-technical customer in the public and private sectors.

2. The quality of debugging or technical security inspection services offered by security organizations varies widely and that minimum standards or statements of performance are infrequently offered or requested.

Interception of Non-Audio Information

It is concluded that under Title III there is no current, effective constraint relative to the availability of equipment or employment of procedures directed to the interception of non-audio information including computer data, satellite and microwave communications links, or information processing machines. There appears to be no reason why protections afforded by Title III should not be extended to encompass interception of non-audio information.

Aids to Physical Surveillance

It is concluded that no control exists under Title III over the physical surveillance devices market because all known manufactured electronic devices are not used for privacy invasion of a clandestine, audio information gathering nature.

RECOMMENDATIONS

Guided by the conclusions drawn during this study, it is recommended that actions be initiated to improve protections afforded the private citizen by:

1. The licensing of surveillance devices manufacturers.

2. The licensing of counter-surveillance or debugging equipment manufacturers.

3. The licensing of individuals or firms who offer to sell the services of counter-surveillance sweeps or debugging.

4. The reduction in availability of disguised devices sold or offered for sale through misrepresentation as under the guise of innocent devices such as "burglar alarms" or "baby monitors".

5. The preparation, dissemination, and fostering of guidelines for law enforcement personnel which provides instruction in the characteristics, handling, and identification of suspect electronic eavesdropping devices; the characteristics and use of countermeasure products and services; and the use and limitations of electronic surveillance.

6. The expansion of Title III legislation regarding the terms and definitions used to describe electronic surveillance devices that includes prohibition of interception of non-audio information and its acquisition through use of electronic devices.

7. The prohibition of publication for distribution of schematics, diagrams, and instruction manuals for the fabrication of eavesdropping devices.

A brief discussion in support of each recommendation follows:

Licensing of Surveillance Device Manufacturers

Current legislation restricts the acquisition of electronic surveillance devices generally to officials of law enforcement and communications common carriers. It lends little support to improving the quality of equipment offered by legitimate electronic device manufacturers. This forces the surveillance equipment prices upward since the producer is prohibited by statute from stockpiling components, engaging in the research and development of better equipment, and assembling and distributing electronic surveillance devices according to normal commercial practices. That is, a manufacturer cannot inventory, mass produce, demonstrate, distribute or promote electronic eavesdropping equipment or offer support services. As a result, new ideas for better products which might allow more effective law enforcement, lower prices, and better quality, are suppressed from entering the legitimate market. Aggravating this situation, according to some manufacturers, is unequal enforcement of the existing law which seemingly permits a few manufacturers to stockpile partially assembled devices and thereby manipulate or avoid the intention of the law. This causes unfair competition among the legitimate and the unethical manufacturers and tends to degrade the character of the entire market. This atmosphere is so severe that

several well-known manufacturers of miniature, body bug transmitters currently use designs and techniques that are ten years old. Analagous devices produced in Europe frequently exhibit better performance, smaller size, and better reliability because of the absence of strict control.

It is recommended that electronic surveillance device manufacturers be licensed. Implementation of this recommendation will allow qualified manufacturers to produce surveillance equipment economically in a carefully controlled environment, thereby providing a means for improving the quality of devices, reducing costs, and stimulating growth and improvement in the overall market without fostering an increase in illegal activity.

Licensing of Counter-Surveillance Equipment Manufacturers

The licensing of countermeasures or debugging equipment manufacturers is long overdue, since the technical security marketplace has been plagued for years by claims of miraculous "bug" or "tap" detecting devices. These far reaching claims border on fraud; but currently there is no effective mechanism to restrict advertising since neither equipment performance standards nor a capable governing body exists to review these claims.

Implementation of this recommendation would provide a means for limiting fraudulent practices by establishing a regulatory licensing structure under the auspices of a standards laboratory that generates and maintains adequate technical standards. These governing standards and licensing arrangements could be structured in a three-tiered heirarchy to provide basic minimum performance levels for equipment in the private sector, a higher level for the law enforcement and industrial sector, and a top level for the most sophisticated customers. The countermeasures equipment advertised and sold would be graded according to measured performance, and public display of this record or certificate would be required in advertising and on equipment offered for sale.

Licensing of Countermeasure Service Organizations

Practitioners of "debugging" or countermeasures sweep services offer a wide range of capability for an equally wide range of prices. These service organizations may charge for services performed which are completely undefined, unstandardized and uncontrolled. Many other commercial service organizations are required, through self-policing actions of trade associations, by regulatory bodies of government, or by statute, to guarantee specific levels of proficiency in the performance of services.

By implementation of this recommendation, improved consumer protection would be effected. A rating, based on licensing examination of the service organization, would be required by reputable service firms and provide the customer with confidence in the quality and cost of services procured.

Availability of Disguised Devices

Readily available, inexpensive electronic devices such as wireless microphones, baby monitors, and telephone controlled audio burglar alarms can be easily converted to audio eavesdropping devices. Usually, the performance of these units can be greatly improved by increasing the number of batteries used or lengthening the antenna.

Implementation of this recommendation would control the availability of devices in this market by requiring new fabrication techniques to prevent device modification, disassembly, retuning, or power increase.

Training of Law Enforcement Personnel

No standard procedures are available to private citizens or police organizations which can be relied upon for credible guidance in the event of discovery of a suspected eavesdropping device or practice which could result in an electronic invasion of privacy.

Implementation of this recommendation provides for the creation of procedural guidelines for police and law enforcement officials to improve the enforceability of current and anticipated laws. By establishing a mechanism through which the technical characteristics of an electronic device may be examined, by assuring that guidelines are developed, disseminated and publicized so that electronic surveillance devices and countermeasures may be made available for proper use by law enforcement personnel, and by training of these personnel when necessary, the use and limitations of electronic surveillance technology can be better understood by law enforcement personnel. Through this enhanced understanding, the private citizen can be assured of competent protection by qualified police assistance.

Interception of Non-Audio Information

The terminology of the Title III statute and the rapid growth in electronics technology has combined to bring to the public attention the lack of coverage provided by the legislation. In practice the eavesdropper has skirted the intent of the law by assembling electronic devices in modular form so that the connection of sub-assemblies results in complete formation of an eavesdropping device. It is recommended that further study be devoted to this problem with the idea of making such assemblages of equipment, due to their existence together and the knowledge that in a precise configuration the modules create an eavesdropping device, presumptive of intent to use the modules for eavesdropping.

Further, it is recommended that a review of terms and definitions in the Title III legislation result in clarification of such word usages as "oral", "aural", or "communication". Without specific reference to Title III context, it is suggested that the concept of "intercept" of "communication" be expanded to encompass all clandestine interception of communications of an oral or non-oral nature.

Publication of Eavesdropping Device Literature

Numerous eavesdropping devices are described in literature that is readily available to the public. These publications are often completely descriptive of device circuitry including design drawings, schematics, parts lists, techniques of fabrication, and integration for system application. These documentation packages are usually offered for sale with no less intention than encouragement to the recipient of the information to manufacture illegal devices.

Implementation of this recommendation would inhibit the dissemination and proliferation of specific data where its utilization may result in Title III violations.

EQUIPMENT CHARACTERISTICS AND CAPABILITIES

1.0 Audio Eavesdropping

Throughout the body of this report the term "audio eavesdropping" is used to mean the surreptitious interception of wire or oral communications. It is accomplished primarily through the use of various electronic devices and technical processes. A complete audio eavesdropping system requires a device that will convert audible sounds into electrical signals and communicate these signals via radio transmitter, wire, or light beam to the eavesdropper. This section of the report describes those devices which are capable of performing all or part of this eavesdropping process and the characteristics and limitations of each device. Initially, the discussion centers on the telephone system and its role in audio eavesdropping technology, but it progresses to include radio transmitters, microphones, tape recorders and optical devices that are used today in various forms of audio surveillance.

1.1 Telephone Systems

The standard telephone functions as a small part of a vast electronic system which is operated by the telephone company. The company provides all of the power to operate the subscriber telephones, the automatic switching equipment which connects one instrument to another, and the various electronic signals which cause dial tones, ringing, and busy signals. Some of these features may be used by the eavesdropper to advantage in telephone surveillance. He may use the voltage present on the wires to supply power to electronic devices, the wires themselves to carry audio signals that have been converted to electrical signals, and the handset as an eavesdropping microphone.

Telephone audio eavesdropping can be accomplished by two methods that involve connecting various electronic devices to this system. The first and most widely publicized method uses wiretap paraphernalia which intercepts conversations directly from the telephone wires and requires no entry into the target premises. The second method is that which uses a portion of the telephone system for room eavesdropping and usually requires physical entry into the premises. This method is possible because the telephone instrument with its associated wires and electronic parts can be made to monitor room conversations with minor electrical modifications. The diagram of a standard telephone instrument is shown in Figure 5. This schematic illustrates portions of the telephone which are susceptible to modification or additions and likewise illustrates the technical complexity of some forms of electronic eavesdropping. Below the diagram is a list of telephone system oriented eavesdropping devices which are included in the discussion presented in this and the following paragraphs.

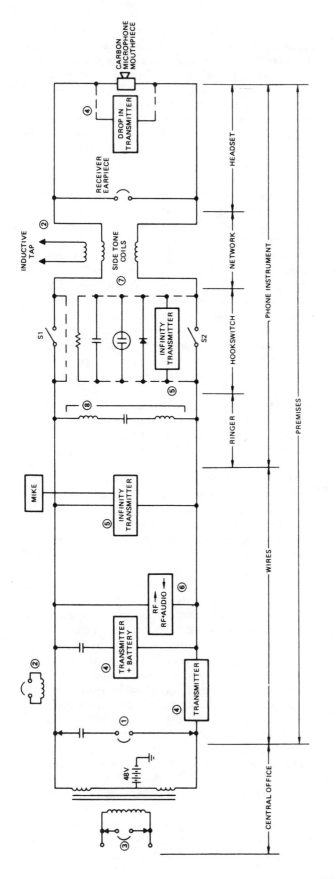

FIGURE 5. TELEPHONE SYSTEM EAVESDROPPING[1]

① DIRECT HARDWIRE TAP ON TELEPHONE LINE
② INDUCTIVE TAPS, ONE EACH ON LINE AND INSTRUMENT
③ DIRECT TAP AT THE TELEPHONE COMPANY EXCHANGE
④ RADIO TAP ON TELEPHONE LINE AND INSTRUMENT

⑤ INFINITY TRANSMITTERS, ONE EACH ON LINE AND INSTRUMENT
⑥ RADIO ENERGY ILLUMINATION
⑦ TELEPHONE MODIFICATIONS
⑧ RESONANT RINGER

[1]S. W. Daskam, "Detection of Clandestine Eavesdropping Devices," p. 92, International Electronic Countermeasures Conference at Edinburgh, Scotland, July 1973.

The standard telephone instrument consists basically of (1) a microphone, or mouthpiece, which converts the speaker's voice into the electrical signals that are sent through the telephone's internal circuitry and out onto the wires; (2) an earpiece, a magnetic device which receives electrical signals from another telephone and converts these signals back into audible sound; and (3) a dial mechanism which generates the electrical pulses used by the telephone company central switching exchange to identify the dialed telephone number. A switch, which ordinarily keeps these components separated from the external lines when the telephone is not being used, is activated by a spring loaded button or lever when the handset is lifted from its cradle. This switch, shown as S1 and S2 in Figure 5, is called a hook-switch. It plays an important role in the practice of telephone audio eavesdropping. The terms, "off-hook", meaning that the telephone is in use, and "on-hook", meaning that the instrument is not being used are commonly used expressions in any discussion regarding the telephone instrument and will be frequently used here to describe the operating status of the instrument. When the telephone handset is lifted off-hook, the line voltage drops from 48 volts to between 6 and 12 volts, and 60 to 100 milliamperes of current flow through the instrument.[2] This current is modulated by sound waves striking the carbon mouthpiece and passed through the telephone's internal circuitry to the outgoing wires or "talk pair". These signals continue through the telephone company's electronic switching system to the receiving telephone. Here, incoming electrical signals are converted back into audible sounds by the magnetic earpiece. By manipulating these features and exploiting their intended purpose, the eavesdropper is assisted in the process of audio surveillance.

1.1.1 Telephone Wiretapping. The term telephone wiretapping describes a procedure or activity which requires the use of several electronic and mechanical pieces of equipment. The process consists of identifying the specific telephone talk pair of interest at some accessible location along the wires, the interception of their electrical signals, and the communication of these signals to the eavesdropper's tape recorder or headphones. The electronic devices which can accomplish the interception and communications portion of this process are numerous and, with the exception of miniature radio tap transmitters, are available to the private sector. Characteristics and specifications of the devices discussed in this section are set forth in Table I.

1.1.1.1 Wire Systems. The initial step in the wiretapping procedure involves the connection of electronic equipment to the telephone wires to retrieve the audio electrical signals. Proper equipment and installation procedures must be used to assure a good quality wiretap and to prevent easy detection by the telephone company or security inspection team. Two methods are used by professionals which are equally difficult to detect. The first uses a wire coil to inductively couple[3] the audio signals from the lines while the second, more conventional method uses a direct wire connection and electronic matching network. The induction coil technique is somewhat difficult to implement, however, because the low level magnetic field which surrounds the operating telephone line produces a correspondingly low signal level output from the sensing coil. The direct wire equipment is much easier to attach, and provides a more reliable and usable output signal, which is readily recordable. Neither of these techniques will disturb the line voltages or current characteristics and alert the target or telephone company. If an improper connection to the telephone line is made, for example, if a tape recorder input were connected directly to the lines, the change in line voltages or normal audio signal could alert the telephone company or subscriber and would most likely result in poor wiretap performance because of the poor electrical match between the recorder input and the telephone line.

After the eavesdropper has successfully intercepted the telephone line's audio signals, they must be communicated to a convenient location for monitoring and possible recording. In telephone company assisted legal wiretapping, the preferred solution is to lease a pair of lines to carry the signal from the target lines to this listening post. This practice also allows the eavesdropper to monitor many lines, if necessary, from the convenience of an office or central monitoring point. At the listening post an assortment of recording equipment and accessories are used which are described in Section 1.1.1.3. The properly installed direct hardwire connection is preferred over most other wiretapping techniques because of its reliability, superior performance, good quality audio, and increased level of security from detection. If not used, the reasons usually relate to the time involved for proper installation or operational restrictions. Items 1, 2, and 3 on Figure 5 illustrate these methods of wiretapping.

1.1.1.2 Radio Systems. Should the eavesdropper be unable to complete the wire communications link between the target telephone lines and the listening post, a second alternative involves use of the radio tap transmitter. These devices are the same as room radio bugging transmitters except they require no microphone, since the audio signals are already in an electrical form, and may use normal telephone line voltages for power, rather than batteries. To intercept the audio signals, the radio tap transmitter may be connected directly to the telephone lines or to an induction coil which senses the magnetic field around the wire or telephone instrument itself.[4] Figure 6 illustrates three types of radio tab transmitter installations. The point of attachment of a radio tap transmitter is arbitrary, limited only by the ability of the eavesdropper to gain access to the telephone system, as the device may be installed within the instrument itself, anywhere along the telephone line within the building, on a telephone pole, or in the wirecloset or terminal room of an office building where many lines are joined to form a cable.[5] Once in place, these radio transmitters send whatever electrical signals are on the telephone line to a remote radio receiver. They are easy to install and are the preferred telephone tap method where the transmitting range is small, generally one to three city blocks and where a leased line or direct wire connection is not possible.

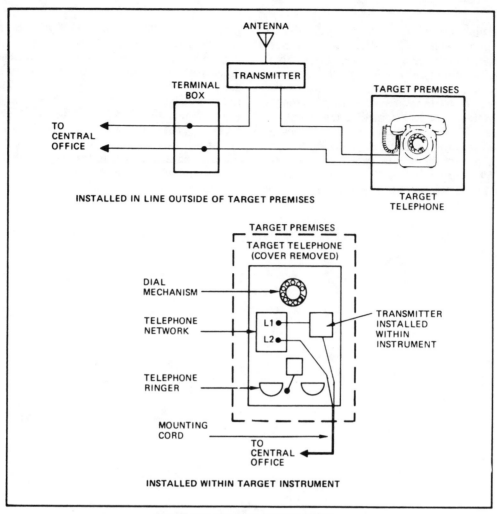

INSTALLED IN LINE OUTSIDE OF TARGET PREMISES

INSTALLED WITHIN TARGET INSTRUMENT

SERIES (IN LINE) TYPE INSTALLATION

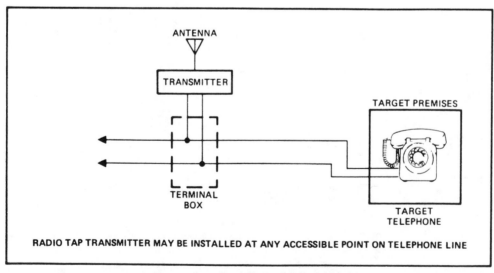

RADIO TAP TRANSMITTER MAY BE INSTALLED AT ANY ACCESSIBLE POINT ON TELEPHONE LINE

PARALLEL (ACROSS LINE) TYPE INSTALLATION

FIGURE 6. RADIO TAP TRANSMITTERS

One very popular radio tap transmitter, the telephone drop-in mouthpiece, is simply placed in the telephone handset after removal of the original mouthpiece unit. Many law enforcement suppliers offer radio tap transmitters which are intended primarily for this purpose though their attractiveness is limited because they may be readily identified through visual inspection inside the handset. During this study, one mail order source was identified that offered an inexpensive "electronic telephone conference call monitor" which could be used as a clandestine radio tap transmitter by an individual desirous of a quick short range, inexpensive tap. Radio devices which are installed within the target telephone require entry to the premises for implacement whereas those connected to the external lines require no entry and suggest different legal implications.

The majority of the radio tap transmitters offered commercially use conventional FM modulation, but a few use more sophisticated modulation techniques to reduce the probability of detection. Other types of modulation are discussed in Section 1.3.2.4. Another means of increasing the security of a radio tap operation is to locate the transmitter far enough from the target telephone so that it is undetectible by a debugging countermeasures team, but close enough to the eavesdropper's receiving set to provide effective operation. Installed in this manner, the radio energy emitted by the transmitter would carry the information as far as a conveniently located listening post, but perhaps not as far as the target instrument, thereby avoiding detection in the area by the security sweep team's radio frequency (r-f) sensing equipment. The smallest radio tap transmitter offered commercially is the size of a corn kernel, "small enough to be inserted within the telephone wire sleeving". This device operates in the VHF region and, according to the manufacturer, will effectively operate over a range of up to 100 yards.

1.1.1.3 Accessories. At the eavesdropper's receiving site, the incoming electrical signals from either wire or radio transmitters are usually recorded on a conventional tape recorder for later playback. Several electronic accessories may be used which permit the eavesdropper to record the telephone numbers dialed by the target along with the date and time. These devices are commonly known as pen registers (or dial impulse recorders) and touch tone decoders. Originally designed for use with dial telephones, these devices record the telephone electrical pulses which are generated during dialing as dots on a strip of paper. The pen register operator simply counts the dots in each dial pulse group to determine the number called. Today these devices are fully electronic and present the operator with the actual number dialed, either printed on paper tape like an adding machine or in a lighted numerical display. Generally, the devices are expensive and not publically available. For the eavesdropper unable to obtain these devices, a multispeed audio tape recorder may suffice as a dial decoder. The tape speed can be reduced after recording a telephone dialing sequence. The pulses may then be counted to determine the telephone number dialed.

Other accessories include two telephone line voltage activated switch devices. One is called a telephone slave, and the other is the cheesebox which is now obsolete.[6] Usually the two wires extending from one side of either device are attached to an accessible telephone line pair with a known number and two other wires are connected to a second telephone line pair. In the case of the slave unit, the second connection is made to the telephone line which is to be monitored or tapped. When the telephone number of the first line is called from any location, the slave will automatically respond to the call by connecting the two telephone lines together, thereby permitting the eavesdropper to wiretap or remotely monitor conversations taking place on the other telephone line. These devices are used by law enforcement agencies when leased lines are not available. They effectively allow several lines to be wiretapped from a single telephone at the listening post, thereby eliminating the requirement for multiple leased lines. The telephone slave tends to be unreliable in practice, however, and occasionally will malfunction causing the eavesdropper's telephone line to be held in an open position. If this occurs, the next time the eavesdropper calls the slave unit, a busy signal is continuously received.

In another application, a slave type device may be connected, not to a second telephone line, but directly to a microphone and amplifier to allow monitoring of room sounds rather than a telephone conversation. This procedure requires that a microphone and amplifier be installed in the target area and that an unused telephone line be available nearby for the connection. At any time, the number of the unused line may be dialed from a remote point, and the eavesdropper will be connected automatically to the microphone to monitor the premises. Some devices offered for law enforcement use contain the slave type switch and microphone prepackaged in a standard telephone connector block.

The cheesebox is similar to a slave in operation but, instead of connecting one telephone line to another for eavesdropping purposes, it connects the two lines and permits two-way conversation between the parties to prevent call tracing. Used in this fashion, the cheesebox can be considered more of an interference to law enforcement than an audio eavesdropping device, and currently little use is found in any sector, since the more efficient, modern call forwarders which are discussed in the following paragraph can be made to serve a similar purpose.

A legitimate and widely used telephone accessory is the call forwarder or re-dialer. The device is connected between two existing telephone lines, and a telephone number is entered electronically into the unit. When a call is received on one telephone line, the unit automatically dials the internally stored second number to reach the desired second telephone. These devices are being increasingly offered by telephone companies and are used by doctors, executives, and others who wish to receive normal incoming calls at a more readily accessible number while away from an office or home. When used in a business environment, these devices frequently have provisions for third party monitoring.

Voltage and voice actuated automatic switching devices are widely used in illegal audio eavesdropping systems. Their function is to sense the changing voltages or audio signals on a telephone line caused by use of the telephone, and thereby automatically turn recording equipment or radio transmitters on and off. This is necessary to conserve recording tape or avoid unnecessary radio transmissions. Voltage actuated devices are readily available as components of some automatic telephone answering devices or telephone secretaries.

The audio amplifier is a fundamental tool in all communications activities. It is on the eavesdropper's list of equipment and is used not only in telephone line tapping but also with microphone systems. Basically, amplifiers serve to increase the relatively small audio signal level which exists on telephone lines, or at the output of a microphone, to a level which is strong enough to be used in the intended manner. An additional amplifier is usually not required for use with a good quality tape recorder because of built-in amplifying circuitry. Audio amplifiers are also used in countermeasures inspections for eavesdropping devices. These small amplifying units with built-in speakers are available from general electronic stores, but do require some type of matching circuitry for use directly on a telephone line.

1.1.2 Telephone Eavesdropping. The previous paragraphs discussed those procedures and devices used by an eavesdropper for telephone wiretapping,

which is limited to the monitoring and recording of actual telephone conversations. This section describes several other devices and techniques which cause separate portions of the telephone instrument to act as part of a room eavesdropping system. Items 5 through 7 in Figure 5, the telephone instrument diagram, show devices discussed in this section which accomplish this purpose. None are intended for the reception of telephone conversations.

1.1.2.1 Infinity Transmitters or Harmonica Bugs. The most widely publicized room eavesdropping device that uses the telephone system is the infinity transmitter or harmonica bug. The name infinity transmitter is derived from the original manufacturer's claim that it could eavesdrop on room conversations from an "infinite" distance by using the telephone system wires. These devices are not really transmitters at all but are tone controlled switches usually coupled with an audio amplifier and microphone. The tone switching mechanism in the transmitter is designed to activate the microphone when it receives an electrical signal or audio tone of a specific frequency over the telephone line. Originally this audio frequency or tone was usually about 440 Hz (a "C" note on a harmonica); because of this the popular name "harmonica bug" was derived.

To operate the infinity transmitter, the eavesdropper dials the target telephone and before the telephone rings, the harmonica is blown or a tone beeper is sounded into the eavesdropper's telephone mouthpiece. (Newer devices are becoming available which use multiple tones to activate the transmitter, thus making detection by sweep teams more difficult.) On the target telephone, the infinity device receives the audio tone and switches the device to answer the target telephone electrically rather than physically. The target telephone should not ring if the eavesdropper is quick enough with the activation signal and if the telephone system itself is designed so that the signal reaches the target instrument without delay. If the target instrument does ring, the eavesdropper may merely wait for the subject to answer, pretend to have dialed the wrong number, and when the target telephone handset is returned to the cradle, quickly activate the infinity device and monitor the room sounds. If the subject uses the telephone to make a call, the eavesdropper hangs up his own telephone and the listening device is disconnected.

Today infinity devices are offered for sale to law enforcement personnel in small, easily installed electronic modules; they are offered to the public also, but not as eavesdropping tools. In many cases, they are advertised as an inexpensive audio burglar alarm that allows the home owner to call his residence telephone while away on a trip and listen for burglars. Infinity devices are installed by entering the premises and making a wire connection to the telephone lines at any point in the area to be monitored, a procedure clearly described by the manufacturer's instruction sheet. The point where the connection is made depends upon the eavesdropper's intentions; it may be installed near or inside the telephone instrument, or in another room apart from the instrument where the line passes on its way to exit the building. Once in place, the device monitors all nearby room conversations when it is activated.

During the course of this study, five different burglar alarm infinity devices were found to be offered for sale in magazines and newspapers. All were described in large advertisements and freely transmitted technical data to indicate that the device is intended for use as a burglar alarm and intrusion detection system, with warnings that the device is not intended for eavesdropping. The following claim describing these devices is representative:

Now you can check your premises anytime from anywhere. This system consists of the monitor unit which plugs into standard telephone jacks supplied with each system. This unit is placed at the site to be monitored. The remote activator will allow you to activate the monitor unit from any dial telephone. The receiver amplifier unit which sets by your bedside telephone continuously monitors your premises even while you are asleep. The telephone never rings. You won't alert a burglar by a ringing phone. The telephone in your office or business won't make the slightest sound. It will set there just as innocently as ever while you safely monitor your premises. WARNING: This is not a bug.

Several performance characteristics of the infinity transmitter should be mentioned, since they greatly influence the application of these devices. Because telephone systems vary in performance and method of operation, identical devices may operate differently on different telephone systems, causing their performance to be inconsistent or unreliable. This situation occurs when the telephone system's audio connection between the two telephones is not completed at the same time the ring signal is sent to the target telephone. This condition prevents the tone switching signal from reaching the target in time to prevent the audible ring and the target telephone must be answered to complete the audio circuit. One major drawback to successful use of these devices occurs because the telephone line appears to be in use to the telephone company's automatic sensing equipment, and all callers to the target telephone number receive the normal busy signal while the infinity device is in use. This may quickly raise questions and alert the subject that something unusual is affecting the telephone line.

The infinity type of device can be easily detected while in operation. Since the telephone line voltage changes when the telephone is used, an operating infinity device causes the voltage to behave in a similar manner. By measuring this voltage change, technicians can determine if an infinity device is active, and by monitoring the line with other audio sensing equipment, may listen to the same audio signals the eavesdropper is receiving. Finally, the eavesdropper has no way of determining in advance if any interesting conversation is transpiring in the target area, and the target premises must be repeatedly monitored, causing suspicious, lengthy or repeated telephone line use.

1.1.2.2 Listen-Backs and Keep-Alives. Two devices which are modifications of the infinity transmitter are known as listen-backs or keep-alives. These devices contain simple electronic components available through conventional electronic retail outlets. They are not tone activated like the infinity device and do require that the subject telephone be answered to operate. These devices must be installed across the hook-switch within the instrument itself and operate by holding the line open between the eavesdropper's telephone and the target telephone after the call is completed and the target telephone handset is returned to the cradle. The target instrument is maintained electrically off-hook by the listen-back device and the eavesdropper may listen with an audio amplifier to conversations taking place in the vicinity of the instrument. To disconnect the device the eavesdropper hangs up, causing a line voltage change which disconnects the device. These devices suffer from the same disadvantage in use as infinity transmitters and, in addition, installation within the telephone instrument may be difficult. They are smaller and less expensive, however, than the harmonica bug because they contain fewer parts. For this reason they may be difficult to identify as eavesdropping devices prior to actual installation within the target telephone.

1.1.2.3 On-Line Microphones. If the eavesdropper has access to a telephone line that passes through the target premises, a device known as an on-line microphone may be used as part of another type of monitoring system. The basic device consists of a microphone, miniature audio pre-amplifier, and matching circuitry. It is connected directly across the telephone wires in the target premises and cannot be dialed or activated from a remote telephone to eavesdrop on the premises. The intercepted radio signal is transmitted only over the unused telephone line pair to the listening post. They are therefore severely range limited, since these signals will not pass through the telephone company's switching exchange. This device, unlike the infinity transmitter and listen-back devices, does not disrupt incoming and outgoing calls; however, because the device is not generally remotely switchable, the intercepted audio signal may be present on the unused wires leaving the target premises and may be detected by a competent countermeasures sweep.

1.1.2.4 Telephone Modifications. In the earlier description of the standard telephone instrument it was pointed out that a telephone consists of an earpiece, mouthpiece and associated circuitry separated from its transmission lines by the hook-switch. The eavesdropping devices discussed to this point make use of the telephone lines and, at the same time, generally exploit the normal operation of the complete system. But an important feature of the telephone instrument of interest to the eavesdropper is the hook-switch within the instrument itself. If the eavesdropper can somehow short-circuit or bypass this switch, the telephone handset will act as an open room microphone.

The process of shorting or bypassing the hook-switch in a manner that does not affect the normal operation of the telephone, but causes the unused telephone to become a microphone, is known as telephone compromising. It is accomplished by the eavesdropper by producing any of numerous electrical circuit changes inside the telephone.

The electrical symbols shown in Figure 5 above location S2, the hook-switch, indicate several possible telephone instrument modifications and are but a few examples of the many changes that are possible. The objective of these changes is generally to activate the telephone's carbon mouthpiece by allowing a small, nearly undetectable amount of direct current to flow through the instrument.

Occasionally, the telephone's earpiece may be made to serve as the eavesdropping microphone because of its magnetic nature which permits it to function not only as an earpiece, but also as a microphone. If the eavesdropper elects to use the earpiece, the electrical signals must be amplified more than signals from the mouthpiece to compensate for its lower level signal output. Once the room audio is passed through the unused instrument into the outgoing lines, the eavesdropper may intercept it only at a point between the modified target instrument and the first telephone company switching exchange. At this interception point the audio information may be monitored by earphones, recorded, or transmitted by radio to a more remote listening post. In addition to the modified telephone instrument, the eavesdropper must use other electronic devices to complete the operational system. Not only must the intercepted room audio from the lines be amplified but also ring voltages from other callers, which are much larger in amplitude than the audio signal being monitored, must be filtered. The electronic devices necessary to accomplish this filtering, detecting, and switching process are relatively unsophisticated and could be reproduced from easily obtainable electronic components. The only remaining consideration is that care be taken not to disturb the normal quiescent electrical status of the telephone line. To alter or disrupt these characteristics would cause the telephone company to investigate the excessive current drains, voltage changes, or line noise and increase the possibility of discovering the eavesdropper's activity.

The compromise of a telephone instrument is one of the few eavesdropping practices which generally requires technical skill and a thorough knowledge of the telephone system for successful implementation. This fact, plus the operating range limitation and the difficulty in selecting the specific line pair of the target instrument from the maze of other wire pairs, causes this eavesdropping technique to be unattractive to many private sector eavesdroppers. Only one commercial manufacturer offers the complete electronic telephone compromise system in a single package to law enforcement agencies.

The modification of single line instruments is far easier than modification of the standard five-button office telephone for two reasons. First, the internal complexity of the multi-line system requires additional skill and experience beyond that required for single line compromise; second, the rotary type line selection switching, commonly found within the office areas equipped with multi-line instruments, prevents the selection of a specific line pair from outside the area. This latter difficulty essentially eliminates the probability that a single, multi-line target instrument would be compromised for an external audio penetration, but leaves some possibility for a penetration from within the internal office switching network, that is, between two instruments sharing a common line extension. Use and knowledge of this eavesdropping technology has been understood for years but only recently has it become of interest to the private sector.

1.1.2.5 Radio Frequency Flooding. An occasional newspaper article mentions a highly sophisticated technique by which a normal telephone can be converted to a room listening device. This esoteric technique is called radio frequency flooding. Although reported to be a threat, it is generally known only to sophisticated electronics experts, is extremely difficult to implement, very range limited, and requires an abundance of costly electronic equipment.[7] As it has little or no application to law enforcement, it will not be discussed here.

1.1.3 Summary of Telephone Device Characteristics. Table I is a summary of data obtained during the course of this study. Its content was obtained from manufacturers' catalogues and through personal interviews.

TELEPHONE DEVICES SUMMARY

	NAME	PRIMARY USE	OPERATING PRINCIPLE	NOMINAL CHARACTERISTICS	COST RANGE IN DOLLARS	PRINCIPAL USER	SUPPLY SOURCE
1.	INDUCTION PICKOFF COIL	TAPPING	DETECTS MAGNETIC FIELD SURROUNDING TELEPHONE INSTRUMENT OR WIRES CONTAINING AUDIO SIGNALS	SIZE: 1/4" x 3/4" DIAMETER	3–10	ALL SECTORS	GENERAL ELECTRONICS OUTLETS
2.	RADIO TAP TRANSMITTER	TAPPING	DETECTS TELEPHONE LINE AUDIO SIGNALS AND TRANSMITS THEM TO A DISTANT RADIO RECEIVER	SIZE: 1/2" x 1" x 1" RANGE: 100–1000 FT	100–350	GOVERN- MENT SECTOR	LAW ENFORCE- MENT EQUIP- MENT SUPPLIERS
3.	TELEPHONE CONFERENCE RADIO TRANSMITTER	TAPPING	SAME AS ITEM NO. 2	SIZE: 1" x 1" x 1" RANGE: 100–300 FT	5–20	PRIVATE SECTOR	MAIL ORDER
4.	DIAL DECODERS AND PEN REGISTERS	IDENTIFICATION OF DIALED NUMBER DURING LINE TAP	COUNTS DIAL PULSES OR DECODES TOUCH TONES	NOT APPLICABLE	900–1500	PRIVATE SECTOR	SAME AS ITEM NO. 2
5.	CALL FORWARDERS AND REDIALERS	AUTOMATIC CALL FORWARDING	DETECTS INCOMING CALL AND REDIALS SECOND TELEPHONE NUMBER	NOT APPLICABLE	TELEPHONE COMPANY LEASED	ALL SECTORS	TELEPHONE COMPANY AND SPECIALIZED ELECTRONICS
6.	SLAVE	TAPPING	AUTOMATICALLY CONNECTS EAVESDROPPER'S TELEPHONE LINE TO TARGET LINE ON COMMAND	SIZE: 1 1/4" x 3" x 1/2"	100–300	GOVERN- MENT SECTOR	SAME AS ITEM NO. 2
7.	CHEESEBOX	PREVENTS LINE TRACING	JOINS TWO TELEPHONE INCOMING LINES WITH SEPARATE NUMBERS TO PER- MIT TWO-WAY CONVERSATION	NOT APPLICABLE	150–250	OBSOLETE	HOMEMADE
8.	INFINITY TRANS- MITTER AND HARMONICA BUG	ROOM EAVESDROPPING	USES TELEPHONE SYSTEM TO CONNECT ROOM MICROPHONE TO LISTENING POST OR EAVESDROPPER	SIZE: 1" x 1/2" x 3/4" RANGE: LIMITED ONLY BY TELEPHONE SYSTEM CAPA- BILITY	350–600	PRIVATE SECTOR	SAME AS ITEM NO. 2
9.	AUDIO BURGLAR ALARM	ROOM EAVESDROPPING	SAME AS ITEM NO. 8	SIZE: 2" x 5" x 6"	200–400	PRIVATE SECTOR	MAIL ORDER OR SECURITY SYSTEM ELEC- TRONIC OUTLETS
10.	LISTEN BACKS AND KEEP ALIVES	ROOM EAVESDROPPING	HOLDS TELEPHONE LINES AND INSTRUMENT OPEN AFTER TARGET HANGS UP	SIZE: 1/8" x 1/16" x 1/8" RANGE: SAME AS ITEM NO. 8	5–100	GOVERN- MENT SECTOR	SAME AS NO. 2
11.	TELEPHONE MODIFICATION COMPONENTS	ROOM EAVESDROPPING	CONVERTS TELEPHONE INTO ACTIVE MICROPHONE WHILE UNUSED	SIZE: 1/8" x 1/16" x 1/16" RANGE: LENGTH OF TELE- PHONE WIRE BETWEEN TAR- GET AREA AND TEL. CO. EX	1–5	GOVERN- MENT SECTOR	GENERAL ELECTRONICS OUTLETS
12.	ACTUATOR SWITCHES	TURN ON AND OFF TAPE RECORDERS	SENSES LINE VOLTAGE OR VOICE AND AUTOMATICALLY CONTROLS TAPE RECORDER	SIZE: 1" x 2" x 3"	100–300	ALL SECTORS	GENERAL ELECTRONICS OUTLETS

TABLE I

1.2 Microphone Systems

Use of a concealed microphone is the oldest of all electronic eavesdropping methods and is still the most reliable approach to clandestine monitoring of room conversations. The advantages over other methods include the system durability, security, and limitless operating life. Properly installed, the "mic and wire" system with switching actuators and several well positioned microphones can be remotely controlled by the eavesdropper to allow monitoring of different, selected areas. Since the wire portion of the system is usually attached directly to a tape recorder or an audio amplifier (headphones may be used for direct monitoring), there is no need for radio transmitters, receivers, or other costly electronic equipment. All components required for the basic system are readily available and offered for sale without restriction in the private sector.

The system performs two functions for the eavesdropper. The microphone converts room sounds into electrical signals, and the wires carry these signals to the eavesdropper. The microphone is usually supplied with its power from the monitoring post, via the same wires that carry the intercepted audio signal to the eavesdropper. These wires could run for several miles, and a distinct advantage is gained by the remote power source, in that once the system is installed there is no need to risk entry to the target premises for the purpose of changing batteries. In addition, this permits the eavesdropper to disconnect the power supply and reduce the probability of detection by a countermeasures team's electrical analysis of the wires exiting the premises. For operation over the several mile range, special wires, pre-amplifiers, and line drivers located near the microphone may be required. The following sections describe several microphone types available today and their application to audio surveillance.

1.2.1 Types of Microphones. The microphone is by no means limited to use with wire systems. The types of microphones described in this section are used with radio transmitters, infinity transmitters, tape recorders and other devices which receive and convert sound to an electrical signal. This point should be kept in mind as the different types are discussed.

1.2.1.1 Carbon Microphones. The original microphone invented by Alexander Graham Bell in 1876 was a carbon microphone. Its durability, reliability, ruggedness and resistance to changes in humidity and temperature still make it a favored device among eavesdroppers. It is used today as the mouthpiece of most standard telephone instruments and because of this availability, it is still quite popular. The carbon microphone suffers somewhat as an eavesdropping device, however, because it needs power to operate. In some installations the power can be supplied from the listening post through the same wires which carry the audio signal but this inconvenience will generally limit the range between the eavesdropper and the target area. This characteristic also prevents the carbon microphone from being used on small battery powered radio bugging transmitters where an attempt is made to keep power consumption low to extend the device's operating life. The physical characteristic that detracts from its usefulness in an eavesdropping system is its size; it tends to be larger than other types of microphones and thus less easily concealed.

The carbon microphone operates in the following manner. A small voltage, perhaps the amount supplied by a single flashlight battery, is connected in series with the terminals of the microphone through a long pair of wires. A few milliamperes of direct current will flow from the battery down one wire, through the microphone and back to the eavesdropper's equipment on the other wire. While this direct current is flowing, the microphone modulates the current in a manner proportional to the sound it receives in the target area. This modulated electrical signal is then separated at the listening post and actively monitored or recorded.

1.2.1.2 Magnetic Microphones. The magnetic or dynamic microphone has characteristics which make it very attractive as an audio eavesdropping tool. These microphones require no power to operate, are usually quite small and convert sound into electrical signals by the movement of a small coil of wire near a permanent magnet. This action generates small electrical signals in the coil proportional to the coil movement caused by the sound vibrations striking a thin diaphragm which is physically connected to the coil of wire.

For eavesdropping purposes, this ability to generate the required electrical signal from room sounds is a very important feature. This means that no power for the microphone is drained from the battery of a radio transmitter, recorder, or other powered device to which it is attached. In the "mic and wire" system, however, this feature is not of value since the electrical signal generated is very small and will not travel very far over a wire without the addition of an amplifier. Nevertheless, magnetic microphones are used in eavesdropping because of their small size, low cost, and high sensitivity. Figure 7 illustrates installation techniques for a variety of microphones[8] used in audio surveillance and one method of "painting" a pair of wires using silver paint. This silver paint is electrically conductive and will carry the microphone's audio output signal to the eavesdropper in the same manner as a wire pair.

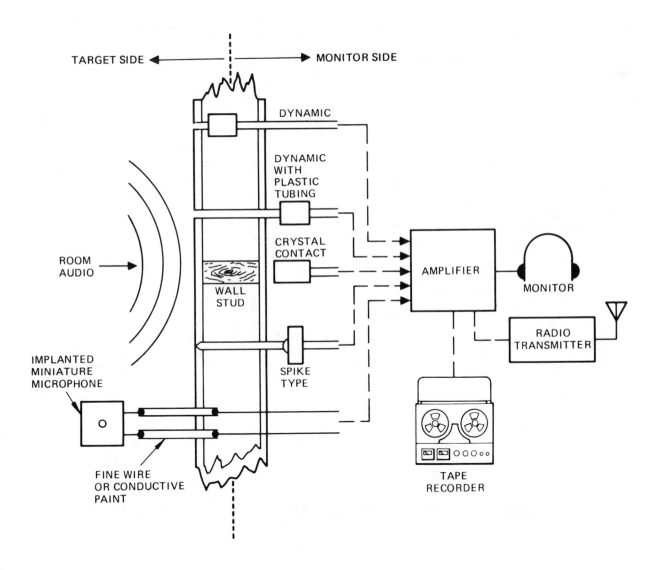

FIGURE 7. VARIOUS MICROPHONES TYPES AND METHODS OF COVERT INSTALLATION

The dynamic microphone is frequently offered by law enforcement equipment suppliers in pre-packaged concealments, such as in cuff links and eye glasses for use with body-worn recorders or radio transmitters, and in electrical wall sockets or appliances for room monitoring installations. These concealed microphones are nominally priced, and a few contain built-in amplifiers to increase the amplitude of electrical signals produced by the microphone for transmission over longer wire paths. Other types of microphones can be easily concealed in these same objects, but generally, the dynamic device is chosen because of its relative advantages over other types.

1.2.1.3 Speakers. The primary function of a speaker is to generate sound from applied electrical signals rather than sense sound and generate an electrical signal output. The ordinary permanent magnet (PM) speakers, commonly used in portable radios, walkie-talkies and stereo systems can be made to serve as an eavesdropping microphone as illustrated in Figure 8. The PM speaker is structurally similar to a dynamic microphone with a coil of wire positioned in a magnetic field. When used as a speaker, electrical current is passed through the coil which vibrates the speaker to produce sound. Most of these speakers show varying degrees of reciprocal performance and can therefore be used as microphones. When acoustical energy impinges on an unused speaker cone and vibrates the coil of wire in the permanent magnet field, small amounts of electrical energy are produced which can be transmitted by radio or over wires to a listening post.[9] This fact is frequently overlooked by many countermeasure sweep teams, and radios, stereo speakers, public address systems and intercom systems frequently go unchecked.

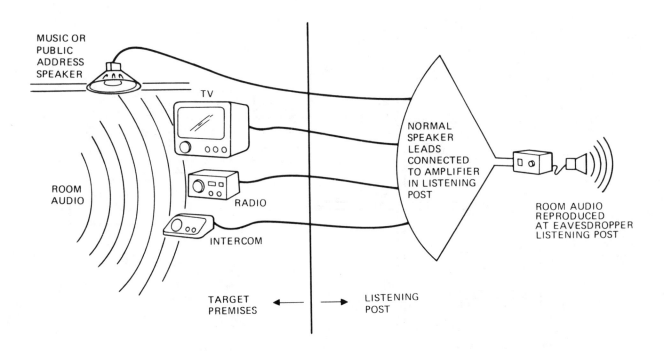

FIGURE 8. MAGNETIC SPEAKERS USED AS SURVEILLANCE MICROPHONES

1.2.1.4 Condenser Microphones. The condenser microphone has gained some popularity in recent years because of its adaptability to high fidelity applications. These microphones are electrical capacitors which, when impacted by acoustic energy, change their electrical characteristics by changing the capacitance of the microphone circuit. These microphones exhibit good response in the spectrum of 30 to 18,000 Hz, the full range of human hearing, but are not generally used for audio surveillance because of the additional circuitry required for proper operation.

1.2.1.5 Electret Microphones. This non-magnetic device is extremely small in size, and has high sensitivity and good frequency response. It is similar in construction to a capacitor type except that a voltage charge is permanently stored internally, and it is the vibration of this charge in response to the room audio which produces the electrical output signal. The electret does require voltage to power a built-in preamplifier, but the power consumed is very low. The electret rivals the magnetic microphones in eavesdropping applications, since it exhibits most of the beneficial characteristics of the magnetic unit and has the advantage of producing larger electrical signals with its built-in amplifier.[10]

1.2.2 Special Purpose Microphones. Performance improvements can be made to the basic microphone to increase its ability to receive low level sounds. Many manufacturers offer different devices which contribute to this enhancement and, therefore, are of interest to the eavesdropper. These primarily include directional microphones such as shotgun or parabolic devices and pneumatic cavity or contact microphones, designed for listening through windows and walls. Each of these is discussed in the following paragraphs.

1.2.2.1 Contact, Spike and Pneumatic Microphones. Figure 7 illustrates the application of the contact or spike microphone, a device long popular with eavesdroppers. This microphone contains a special crystal which, when slightly compressed, will produce a very small electrical signal. If it is placed against a vibrating wall or window pane or attached to a rigid probe which is touching one of these vibrating surfaces, the crystal will produce small electrical signals which correspond to the vibrations. If these vibrations are caused by room conversation sounds, the electrical signal will correspond to those sounds. The signals generated in this manner are small and are of insufficient strength to travel far over wires. These devices tend to be fragile and are not able to stand temperature, shock, and humidity changes, but are sometimes used today in illegal eavesdropping activities.

The pneumatic cavity microphone is an electronic version of the glass tumbler against the wall, historically recognized as one method of monitoring adjacent room conversations. This microphone is substantially superior however and operates by using a specially constructed small cavity which in general is highly responsive to surface vibrations at the audio frequencies found in human speech. This cavity is used in conjunction with a conventional microphone to enhance its performance and force its output to correspond to wall surface or window vibrations rather than a direct sound input. Though several manufacturers offer these microphone systems publically as electronic stethescopes or cavity microphones, little familiarity with audio devices of this nature was found in the private sector.

1.2.2.2 Shotgun and Parabolic Microphones. The shotgun and parabolic type devices[11] are used by the entertainment and sports industries and occasionally by law enforcement personnel with varying results. The parabolic microphones operate by concentrating the audio energy gathered over an area the diameter of the parabolic reflector, typically 1.5 to 3 or 4 feet, onto a conventional microphone. The large area of the reflector plus its shape causes audio energy received at the microphone to be much greater from one direction than that which would be received by the microphone alone. These devices, under ideal quiet conditions can retrieve normal conversation from a distance of 300 feet, but in practical use are somewhat limited because of background interference such as wind and ambient noises. Some audio equipment companies offer parabolic microphones on a rental basis for $15.00 per day or $30.00 per week, as well as the briefcase to carry all of the equipment, recorders, and audio amplifiers.

From a practical viewpoint, the parabolic microphone is only usable where its large size would not be alerting to the target and where there is a free audio path between the target and the surveillance system. One conventional scenario satisfying these limitations would be the night time operation in an open field or park with the target engaged in a conversation in an extremely quiet environment.

Another directional device is the shotgun microphone which shares many directional characteristics with the parabolic unit. It receives audio from a specific direction through the use of an arrangement of various length tubes. These units tend to be somewhat bulky and may be several feet in length, requiring a tripod or other fixture to hold them in alignment with the target. They must be used in an open environment much the same way as the parabolic device and tend to be slightly more directional and therefore possibly more speaker selective. Shotgun microphones can be very costly but they do perform fairly well over short ranges and in most cases are superior to the parabolic microphone. During the survey, only one of these devices was found in a law enforcement agency and it was essentially non-operational.

1.2.3 Microphones Devices Summary. Table II presents a summary of microphone device characteristics.

MICROPHONE DEVICES SUMMARY

TYPE	USE	OPERATING PRINCIPLE	NOMINAL CHARACTERISTICS	COST RANGE IN DOLLARS	SOURCE
CARBON	TELEPHONE MOUTHPIECE, AUDIO SECURITY SYSTEMS	VARIES CURRENT FLOW ACCORDING TO AUDIO RECEIVED	1" TO 3" DIAMETER	$1 − 5	GENERAL ELECTRONIC OUTLETS
DYNAMIC	GENERAL WIDE USE	GENERATES ELECTRICAL SIGNALS ACCORDING TO AUDIO RECEIVED	1/2" TO 2" DIAMETER	$2 − 25	GENERAL ELECTRONIC OUTLETS
ELECTRET	GENERAL WIDE USE	GENERATES ELECTRICAL SIGNALS ACCORDING TO AUDIO RECEIVED	1/4" TO 1/2" DIAMETER	$2 − 25	GENERAL ELECTRONIC OUTLETS
CRYSTAL, SPIKE AND CONTACT	SENSE WINDOW AND WALL VIBRATIONS	CONVERTS VIBRATIONS INTO ELECTRICAL SIGNALS	VARIOUS	$5 − 50	LAW ENFORCEMENT SUPPLIERS
PNEUMATIC CAVITY	SENSE WINDOW AND WALL VIBRATIONS	CONVERTS VIBRATIONS INTO ELECTRICAL SIGNALS	3" − 7" DIAMETER	$50 − 150	LAW ENFORCEMENT SUPPLIERS
SHOT GUN AND PARABOLIC	DIRECTIONAL SENSING OF SOUND, SPORTS, ENTERTAINMENT	FOCUSES SOUND VIBRATIONS COMING FROM ONE DIRECTION	18" − 36" DIAMETER OR 3' TO 6' IN LENGTH RANGE − 60−300 FEET	$100 − 5,000	AUDIO SYSTEMS OUTLETS
CAPACITOR OR CONDENSER	GENERAL WIDE USE	CONVERTS AUDIO INTO CORRESPONDING VARIATIONS CIRCUIT FREQUENCY	1/2" TO 2" DIAMETER	$10 − $100	GENERAL ELECTRONIC OUTLETS

TABLE II

1.3 Radio Eavesdropping Devices

Radios are electronic devices which transmit or receive radio energy to convey information. The device which transmits or sends this energy is the transmitter, and the device which detects or receives this energy is the receiver. The radio transmitter accomplishes two functions: it generates a continuous radio signal at one selected operating frequency and it modulates this frequency with audio signals provided to it by a microphone, amplifier, and modulation circuitry. The resulting electrical energy contains both the audio and high frequency radio signals and is radiated from an antenna. This energy may be sensed by the companion radio receiver which demodulates it, leaving only the audio which is amplified sufficiently to operate headphones or a speaker.

The miniature radio transmitter and its companion receiver are the basic elements of a radio eavesdropping system. Characteristics of this system such as power, frequency, and modulation determine performance in an actual operation. This section reviews characteristics of devices which are used for this purpose.

1.3.1 Inexpensive Devices. Inexpensive transmitter devices cannot be clearly labeled as primarily useful for eavesdropping or bugging. Because of this fact, their sale is not controlled by Title III legislation and they are available from many sources, including hobby stores, audio electronics and communications equipment outlets, and mail order houses. Due to this availability, they are the most widely used and misused eavesdropping devices in the private sector. This group of devices includes wireless microphones, baby monitors, wireless intercoms, and telephone conference monitors, all of which are offered for sale at prices of $5.00 to $20.00.

These devices are relatively small, crude from a technical standpoint, and they will not operate over very long distances. The transmitter power output is generally controlled by Federal Communications Commission (FCC) regulation, and their frequency of operation is always in or very near the commercial AM or FM broadcast bands. Devices of this nature tend to perform unreliably, and frequency instability is a common problem requiring the eavesdropper to retune the receiver continuously to maintain reception. Most devices may be easily altered by the eavesdropper to improve performance or transmission range. The wireless microphone transmitter, the most popular of these inexpensive devices, is described in the following paragraph and is followed by a brief discussion of devices which are easily fabricated by the technically skilled eavesdropper.

1.3.1.1 Wireless Microphone Transmitters. One manufacturer offers a wireless baby nurse transmitter and an FM wireless telephone transmitter; the latter permits group telephone listening by transmitting both sides of the telephone conversations over moderate distances within a home to an FM broadcast radio receiver. This supplier also advertises an AM wireless telephone amplifier which will broadcast to an AM broadcast radio receiver, but this unit is slightly larger, measuring 1.5 x 1.25 x 1 inch, whereas the previous device measured only 1 inch in diameter and 0.5 inches high. Two other suppliers offer wireless microphone modules for under five dollars, one each for use with FM and AM radio receivers. These are the least expensive of the devices identified during this study and are similar in quality to those offered for about $20.00 by a mail order company located on the west coast. Most of these devices are imported and are allowed to operate by FCC regulations because their transmission range is very short, about 50 to 100 feet. Their usefulness as eavesdropping devices can be significantly enhanced, however, by lengthening the antenna or adding another battery in series for greater range. Another modification is to change the frequency until it is outside the broadcast band to prevent accidental detection. Any of these procedures are well within the capability of an eavesdropper with very little technical skill.

1.3.1.2 Fabrications. For the more technically inclined eavesdropper, unable to buy devices legally, there is a wide choice of semi-completed devices which provide better quality and a more sophisticated end product than those just described. It is possible to procure through various mail order outlets text books or technical journals and wiring diagrams for most basic electronic eavesdropping devices. The necessary electronic parts or preassembled modules can be obtained from many television repair shops or electronic equipment suppliers. Using these aids and equipment, the eavesdropper can build devices similar to those offered to law enforcement officials. Even the legitimate law enforcement suppliers frequently use these preassembled electronic modules, such as r-f oscillators, modulators and amplifiers, to fabricate a desired eavesdropping device. The individual who elects to develop quality eavesdropping transmitters does require a considerable amount of electronic equipment which can be quite costly; therefore, the scope of this activity is thought to be more limited than is widely believed.

1.3.2 Drop Transmitters. The battery powered room transmitters are generally used by law enforcement officials for eavesdropping operations where a quick installation is required. These devices are known as drop or quick plant transmitters and always have a finite operating life which requires that they be regularly retrieved for battery replacement. They are also used as body transmitters for security or protection purposes as well as for one party consensual monitoring. Several manufacturers offer preconcealed transmitters already packaged into objects such as ashtrays, picture frames, pen and pencil sets, and cigarette lighters. A discussion of these battery powered radio devices follows.

1.3.2.1 Miniature Devices. The smallest commercially produced transmitters identified during this study are manufactured in Europe and, as described by the manufacturer's catalogue, are the size of a corn kernel, without microphone or battery. This particular device, described previously in Section 1.1.1.2, was inserted in a telephone line or was used with an optional microphone and operated in the VHF frequency band with effective transmission range of up to 100 yards. The smallest device manufactured in the U.S. for the law enforcement community is the size of an aspirin tablet, including microphone and battery, and costs approximately $2,000. Much less expensive FM transmitters are also manufactured in the U.S.; they cost only $30, measure 1.5 x 0.5 x 0.5 inches, and transmit up to 350 feet. These devices are not generally attractive to the law enforcement community because of their poor reliability and lack of frequency stability. The European source of small devices appears to be quite large, and numerous devices were identified in the one cubic inch size range which operate over a wide band of frequencies. These transmitters have good performance characteristics and are designed to operate from ten hours to ten days in a choice of bands ranging from 100 to 250 MHz or 400 to 475 MHz. Some larger devices were also identified which typically measured 2.5 x 1.5 x 1 inches including batteries and have an effective range of up to one half mile.

Two principle U.S. suppliers produce large radio eavesdropping transmitters. This is not because of the manufacturer's limited technical ability, but because of the poor economic return on the investment required to produce a smaller surveillance device. The cost for small transmitters, when produced on a per order basis, is at least $400 per device, which limits their extensive application. There are numerous other U.S. manufacturers producing relatively small transmitters in the 1 x 1 x 2 inch size which transmit up to one quarter mile for periods of 48 to 60 hours. These room eavesdropping devices are usually limited in operation to the standard FM broadcast band and are not suita-

ble for secure, covert law enforcement applications. Because of their size most sub-miniature devices offered to law enforcement are not crystal controlled and are, therefore, susceptible to frequency instability just as the larger, inexpensive devices already discussed. The larger devices used by law enforcement are nearly always crystal controlled and avoid this instability problem. New miniature crystals, however, are permitting this technology to be applied more readily in small units. Generally, any battery powered radio transmitting device is not restricted to a single mode of application and frequently one device is adaptable for use as either a quick drop room transmitter or a body-worn or agent transmitter.

1.3.2.2 Agent Transmitters. Generally, the agent or body transmitter is larger, more powerful and better constructed than the drop-in transmitter. Over two dozen manufacturers produce these devices which emit signals with power outputs of 20 mw to one watt over frequency ranges from 30 to 500 MHz. These devices are usually cigarette pack size including batteries and are designed to operate from satchels or coat pockets. The manufactured quality of these transmitters is better than that of many smaller devices, and most have crystal controlled frequencies for improved stability. One well known electronic equipment manufacturer claims to produce a device weighing only 5.5 ounces, measuring 2.3 x 3.3 x 0.75 inches excluding the antenna with a power output of 200 milliwatts. This performance is sufficient for a transmission range of one quarter mile under most conditions.

Another large manufacturer produces a system which is broken into two packages, one to be attached under each arm. This crystal controlled system also operates in the VHF range and, according to the manufacturer, has a power output of 1 watt. It weighs one half pound including batteries. The effective range of this device could be over five miles under very favorable conditions. The highest powered surveillance transmitter identified during this study operates in the 137-175 MHz frequency spectrum, produces 5 watts of power and measures approximately 2 x 1 x 4 inches.

1.3.2.3 Concealment Packages. Small radio transmitters are frequently concealed in various household or office fixtures, the most common of which are electric sockets or "cube taps". In this configuration, normal household power is supplied directly to the transmitter which permits a permanent installation. These concealed devices normally transmit a signal over a distance of 700 to 1200 feet and cost from $200 to $400.

Quality prepackaged transmitters are available from Europe in ball point pen and pencil configurations, with transmittinq ranges up to 100 yards and 70 hours of operating life using standard hearing aid batteries. The power output of these devices is generally in the 100 milliwatt region which, according to the manufacturer, provides an operating range of up to one half mile in an ideal situation, but usually less in a noisy radio environment. Some concealments physically prohibit the use of an effective antenna, which limits the performance of many of these transmitters. Frequently the antenna, which should be on the order of 1 to 3 feet long, is only a few inches long and regardless of the transmitter power, the device's operating range is limited. The use of concealment packages was not found to be prevalent among the law enforcement and federal communities, principally because of the fact that prepackaged concealments are not suited to most operational requirements. Generally, concealments are only useful when used with similar furnishings or as precise duplicates of those found in the target area.

1.3.2.4 Modulation Techniques. All of the radio transmitters described in this section must modulate their basic operating frequency to convey audio information to the eavesdropper's radio receiver. (In the *Review of Terminology* section of this study, the concepts of AM and FM modulation are discussed.) Occasionally, surveillance transmitters use more sophisticated methods, such as sub-carrier modulation.

Sub-carrier modulation is attractive to the eavesdropper because it is not easily detected with the conventional receiver, and devices are not too difficult to produce. These devices operate by combining intercepted room audio with one low frequency signal and then recombining this resulting signal with a higher frequency radio signal. For example, rather than modulating the audio signal directly onto the main high frequency radio carrier as normally done, it is modulated onto a very low frequency signal such as one at 75 KHz. This is the sub-carrier frequency. The high frequency radio signal is then modulated with the combined low frequency and the desired audio message. The resulting radio signal is very complex and the buried audio message is not detectable by a conventional radio receiver.

To demodulate this signal at the receiver the reverse steps are performed. The basic signal is demodulated twice, once to obtain the 75 KHz sub-carrier signal and a second time to obtain the desired audio signal. This generally requires two radio receivers, one to detect the high frequency main carrier signal and another to detect the very low frequency sub-carrier signal. Sub-carrier transmitters are occasionally used by the government sector because of the increased difficulty of detection.

An operational procedure which is popular among many eavesdroppers is the practice of "snuggling". Regardless of the radio device power, frequency, modulation, or size, an additional level of security can be provided by carefully setting the frequency of the eavesdropping transmitter adjacent to that of a large, high-powered radio station. This is especially useful when using devices which transmit in the commercial FM broadcast band. By setting the transmitter frequency in this manner, the signal in most cases cannot be received by a standard broadcast receiver. The AFC (automatic frequency control) circuit of a standard receiver causes it to automatically select the strongest of two signals and reject the weaker of the two. The eavesdropper must use a modified broadcast receiver which can select the weaker signal.

This is an example of the more sophisticated technology available, but one which is beyond the capabilities of the private sector eavesdropper due to high cost and complexity. The pulse code or digital process is used occasionally in secure governmental communications systems, since digital signals can be easily scrambled or encrypted.

1.3.3 Carrier Current Devices. Below the AM commercial broadcast portion of the radio frequency spectrum is a region identified as very low frequency (VLF). A different type of audio surveillance transmitter is manufactured which operates in this region but uses the electric power lines or telephone lines for transmission of the signals. These FM modulated devices operate between 50 KHz and 300 KHz. At these frequencies very little radio energy is radiated into space. What these signals will do, however, is to move along almost any wire path, including regular electric powerlines. These transmissions are known as carrier current transmissions because of this characteristic. This method of communications is used by many of the wireless intercoms sold commercially and a few audio eavesdropping transmitters.

Carrier current transmitters are usually prepackaged into electrical appliances, lamps, and wall sockets. They are not considered to be sophisticated but are modestly expensive when purchased through a law enforcement supplier. The less expensive devices may be fabricated by repackaging a commercial wireless intercom. Figure 9 illustrates the application of carrier current type devices.

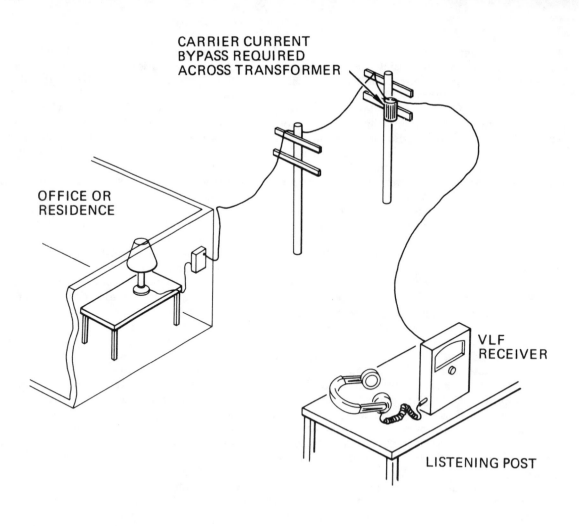

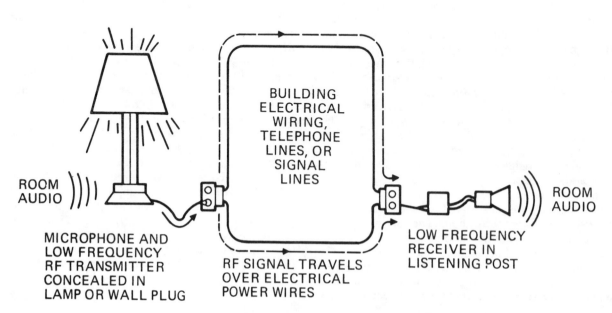

ROOM AUDIO

ROOM AUDIO

MICROPHONE AND
LOW FREQUENCY
RF TRANSMITTER
CONCEALED IN
LAMP OR WALL PLUG

RF SIGNAL TRAVELS
OVER ELECTRICAL
POWER WIRES

LOW FREQUENCY
RECEIVER IN
LISTENING POST

FIGURE 9. CARRIER CURRENT TRANSMITTER

Eavesdropping devices which use carrier currents offer one principal advantage over those which transmit through space. They are not normally detectible by radio receivers or other r-f sensing, debugging equipment, since they radiate little energy. A disadvantage, however, is that the transmissions may be blocked by power transformers which exist regularly in an electric powerline distribution network. This feature can severely limit the range of a carrier current transmitter, and this device is only used in situations where the listening post is located within a short distance from the bugging device. To determine effective range the eavesdropper may wish to run tests, because in many power systems throughout the country, power transformers are made to pass carrier current transmissions and not block them. If this is the case, the range may be several blocks. The reason for this bypass feature is that power companies themselves use these currents for remote switching and load control. The practice of bypassing power transformers may be common for the power companies, but it is a dangerous activity for the eavesdropper to undertake, so the existence of an unauthorized bypass is most unlikely.

The use of carrier current devices on other than power lines is less common. A limited range audio system could be made to operate in a similar fashion over telephone lines, intercom lines, public address systems or security system wires.

1.3.4 Microwave Devices. Devices operating outside the standard radio broadcast frequency ranges tend to be more secure because the receiver needed for reception may not be readily available. A few manufacturers offer eavesdropping devices that operate at frequency ranges above 500 MHz. These units tend to be very expensive because of their complex design and difficult fabrication. The science of microwave radio signal propagation is important and significantly affects the utility of these surveillance transmitters. These high frequency radio signals have difficulty passing through many building materials, such as concrete and brick, and for this reason the transmitted signals should be directed at the receiving site over a path where there are no solid objects to block the way.

1.3.5 Passive Reflectors. This group of radio devices will operate for an indefinite period, offer a high level of security, and require no batteries or other power source. These transmitters are strictly passive. The first publicity associated with eavesdropping devices of this nature occurred in 1952, when it was discovered that a carving of the Great Seal of the United States, a gift of the Russian government hanging in the American Embassy in Moscow, contained such a device. This device operated at 330 MHz and was a small metallic capsule three-quarters of an inch in diameter with a nine inch antenna. Figure 10 illustrates such a device. The complete system includes a high powered radio transmitter which beams its signal at this reflecting capsule and a receiver to receive the reflected signals carrying the audio information. These capsule devices act as radio signal reflectors which capture and add the audio signal during the process of reflection. The devices accomplish this function by making one end of the capsule a very thin metallic diaphragm which vibrates with the room sounds. The signal is reflected from this vibrating surface and carries the modulated radio signal to the receiver for recovery of the audio.[12]

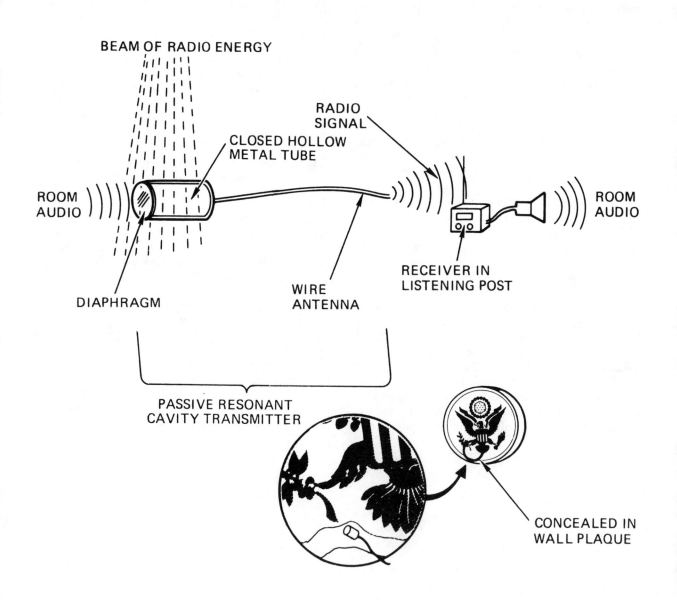

BEAM OF RADIO ENERGY

RADIO SIGNAL

CLOSED HOLLOW METAL TUBE

ROOM AUDIO

ROOM AUDIO

DIAPHRAGM

WIRE ANTENNA

RECEIVER IN LISTENING POST

PASSIVE RESONANT CAVITY TRANSMITTER

CONCEALED IN WALL PLAQUE

FIGURE 10. PASSIVE CAVITY TRANSMITTER

1.3.6 Remote Switch Receiver. The switch receiver is a remote radio controlled device that can be used advantageously with any eavesdropping radio device. Sophisticated remote radio control units are sold through many electronics suppliers for a multitude of purposes including control of water irrigation systems, activation of portable telephone call pagers, as well as audio eavesdropping devices. This device provides the eavesdropper with an ability to control the operating time of room monitoring equipment and achieve two distinct advantages. The eavesdropper can conserve battery power and reduce chances of detection by a sweep team by turning the transmitter on only during a time of interest.

To use the remote switch the eavesdropper attaches the device between the room bug and its batteries. Rather than physically turning the bug on, the unit is electronically activated from the remote point by turning on the control transmitter.

1.4 Tape Recording Systems

The tape recorder is a basic tool of audio surveillance and is found in all sound laboratories of the law enforcement community. It is used to preserve evidence gained through electronic surveillance and to record statements and interviews. Its commercial availability and the adaptability to private sector eavesdropping makes the tape recorder one of the most widely used surreptitious audio penetration devices. For the purposes of this study the information gathered regarding recorder technology was divided into two categories: briefcase systems, and miniature special purpose systems.

1.4.1 Briefcase Concealment Packages. Briefcase systems are generally packaged cassette tape recorders, or occasionally a reel-to-reel unit, built into an attache case. The system may contain a variety of features including voice controlled recorder switches; microphones built into latches; hidden, pressure sensitive on/off switches; and radio receivers. Some packaged systems also include surveillance receivers and are designed to be used as a listening post in conjunction with a radio transmitter. Catalogue advertisements may read typically as follows:

Smartly styled streamline attache case with sub-miniature sensitive microphone concealed inside. The extremely sensitive pickup can cover an entire room, automobile or street conversation. The recorder turns on and off with a movement of a normal open and close latch above the combination lock and most any recorder can be used along with the standard cassettes.

Carrying a briefcase containing a small cassette recorder into a business meeting or sensitive negotiation, or leaving it unobtrusively behind after an office visit, are popular methods employed by eavesdroppers desiring to obtain valuable information. These systems cost between $500 and $1500 depending upon the included options.

1.4.2 Miniature Devices. The smallest recorder identified during the survey was a $2500 European unit claimed by the manufacturer to be the size of a cigarette lighter and to operate for several hours. The miniature recorders most commonly available to the domestic market and law enforcement community have the dimensions of a king-sized package of cigarettes. As an example, one eastern manufacturer supplies a recorder measuring 2 x 3.5 x 1 inch, with one hour recording on each side of a tape cartridge, weighing 5.5 ounces. This particular unit is priced under $500. The next larger device is a widely advertised tape recorder weighing 11 ounces which records 45 minutes per side of tape. This recorder measures 5 x 2.75 x 1 inch.

The advertised prices for identical, domestically manufactured tape recorders frequently varied between $600 and $1000. The true value of these systems is very difficult to ascertain without actual laboratory performance evaluations.

A miniature tape recorder of a well-known Japanese manufacturer is priced at approximately $125. This small unit is hand-held and measures 2.87 x 1.5 x 3.87 inches with built-in microphone, batteries, automatic shut-off switch, and excellent frequency characteristics. This recorder is one of the many pocket secretary devices that are now available from a number of manufacturers. They are commonly used in the surveillance business and are becoming even more popular as their length of operation increases and their size reduces to the point where they can be quickly and easily concealed in fixtures or room furniture. These miniature recorders with voice actuated switches are becoming the "quick-plant" devices of the future as they can only be discovered by careful, physical inspection and may foil radio sweep inspections.

1.5 Optical Directional Systems

Surveillance systems that operate using directional beams of light energy represent another dimension in eavesdropping technology. These systems may use laser or infrared beams, but it is the laser which holds a unique position among electronic surveillance devices because of its futuristic and apparently sinister nature.

The laser has been maligned by casting it in the role of a surveillance device because of a lack of understanding of the laser-surveillance concept on the part of the general public. There are two basic types of light beam devices whose characteristics and applicability to the surveillance market vary widely. Small solid state devices generally called light emitting diodes (LED) can be manufactured to produce invisible infrared or visible light. These

LED devices are commonly used in display of numbers in pocket calculators and electronic wrist watches. Solid state LEDs produce a fairly wide energy beam which generally spreads more rapidly with range than beams produced by lasers. The laser is much more expensive than the LED and produces a tight, coherent beam of visible or invisible energy. The beams produced by these devices can transmit greater distances and suffer a lesser degree of degradation due to beam spreading.[13]

The device producing non-coherent energy can be used in communication transmission links instead of radio transmitters. For example, a small semiconductor LED, coupled with a microphone, power supply, and modulator, could be used as a covert transmitter. When amplified, the voice modulated current or voltage produced by the microphone could modulate the light emitted by the LED. The modulated beam could then be detected by a sensitive optical device some distance from the transmitter and the audio signal retrieved. This is illustrated in Figure 11. The detection of this type of device is extremely difficult, if the installation is well made and the device is protected from discovery by physical inspection or daylight background.

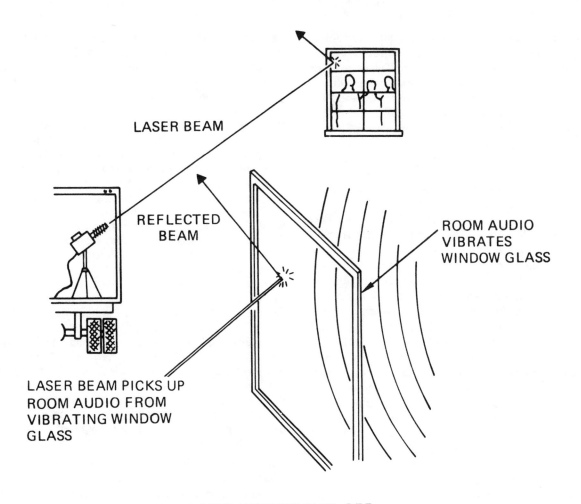

LASER BEAM

REFLECTED BEAM

ROOM AUDIO VIBRATES WINDOW GLASS

LASER BEAM PICKS UP ROOM AUDIO FROM VIBRATING WINDOW GLASS

LASER WINDOW PICK-OFF

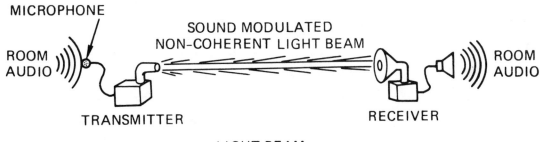

MICROPHONE

SOUND MODULATED NON-COHERENT LIGHT BEAM

ROOM AUDIO

ROOM AUDIO

TRANSMITTER

RECEIVER

LIGHT BEAM COMMUNICATIONS LINK

FIGURE 11. OPTICAL AUDIO EAVESDROPPING

The solid state light beam devices which produce energy in the infrared and visual spectrum are easily obtained, as are the photo cell detectors or receivers at a listening post. Systems are produced for the commercial market which are designed for short range, private data links, internal to building complexes, for short range transmission of audio and television communications. The use of solid state optical devices is generally restricted to this type of application because of their range limitation. These systems are not particularly adaptable to clandestine eavesdropping systems.

Recently, an article in the *Washington Post* newspaper described "the tremendous threat" presented by the telephone company's move to use light emitting diodes in push-button telephones for illumination. It would be technically possible to modulate, with the audio in the telephone instrument, one of these light emitting diodes so that a detector in the ceiling above the telephone could capture the conversation and transmit this information to a listening post. Such an installation could be demonstrated in a laboratory. But from a practical standpoint, the complexities of detector location and telephone instrument manipulation imply that the system is operationally impractical. (A countermeasures or protective action taken by the user of the telephone would simply consist of placing the hand over the illuminated button or removing the light generating devices.)

The coherent laser, such as that available from many manufacturers as laboratory equipment, can be used to detect the minute vibrations which exist in a window pane as a result of nearby room conversation. The coherent laser is used because the small window vibrations cause detectable shifts in the incident beam's wave length. These shifts are then carried on the return beam back to the receiving site where they are demodulated to recover the room audio. This technique is illustrated in Figure 11. Some real problems exist with this laser window-bounce technique of audio surveillance which make its use difficult and expensive. Noises, such as traffic noises, building vibrations due to machinery, air conditioners, fans, running water, plumbing and wind, impart substantial vibrations into the window surface. To retrieve small audio vibrations from this maze of signals is not a reliable or practical source of audio intelligence.

In summary, the laser is not a cost effective device and no evidence or verification of the existence of a laser surveillance system was found. In general, during the course of the study, detailed knowledge of these systems was found to be quite limited, and information was frequently found only in newspaper articles. In contrast to this, however, the use of the solid state devices as a transmission link in surveillance activity is not impractical, since these devices are readily available and no extraordinary technical understanding is required to convert them into an operational eavesdropping system.

1.6 Summary of Eavesdropping Device Characteristics

Table III summarizes characteristics of various eavesdropping devices.

EAVESDROPPING DEVICES SUMMARY

	DEVICE NAME	PRIMARY USE IN EAVESDROPPING	OPERATING PRINCIPLE	NOMINAL CHARACTERISTICS	COST RANGE IN DOLLARS	PRINCIPAL USER	SUPPLY SOURCE
1.	ASPIRIN TABLET MINIATURE DROP-IN TRANSMITTER	CONCEALABLE EAVESDROPPING DEVICE	SENSES ROOM AUDIO AND MODULATES INTERNALLY GENERATED RADIO SIGNAL FOR TRANSMISSION	SIZE: 1/4″ x 1/8″ x 1/4″ RANGE: 200 – 800 FT FREQUENCIES TO 150 MHz	$2000.00	UNKNOWN	LAW EN-FORCEMENT SUPPLIERS
2.	BODY TRANSMITTER	AGENT SECURITY AND EVIDENCE CORROBORATION	SAME AS ITEM NO. 1	SIZE: 2″ x 3/4″ x 3″ RANGE: 500 – 1500 FT FREQUENCY: 50-150 MHz	$350-$650	LAW ENFORCE-MENT	LAW EN-FORCEMENT SUPPLIERS
3.	DROP-INS AND PRE-PACKAGED CONCEALMENTS	QUICK PLANTS OR INSTALLATION IN TARGET AREA	SAME AS ITEM NO. 1	SIZE: 1″ x 1″ x 1/2″ RANGE: 200 – 1500 FT FREQUENCY: 50-500 MHz	$100-$500	LAW ENFORCE-MENT	LAW EN-FORCEMENT SUPPLIERS
4.	TELEPHONE TAPS	TELEPHONE RADIO TAPPING	TRANSMITS TELEPHONE LINE ELECTRICAL SIGNALS TO DISTANT RADIO RECEIVER	RANGE: 200 – 1500 FT FREQUENCY: 50-500 MHz	$150-$350	LAW EN-FORCEMENT	LAW EN-FORCEMENT SUPPLIERS
5.	WIRELESS MICROPHONES	ROOM EAVESDROPPING	SAME AS ITEM NO. 1	SIZE: 1″ x 1/2″ x 2″ RANGE: 50-100 FT FREQUENCY: 88-108 MHz	$10-$25	PRIVATE SECTOR	HOBBY AND MAIL ORDER
6.	BABY MONITORS	ROOM EAVESDROPPING	SAME AS ITEM NO. 1	SIZE: 1″ x 1/2″ x 2″ RANGE: 50-100 FT FREQUENCY: 88-108 MHz	$10-$25	PRIVATE SECTOR	HOBBY AND MAIL ORDER
7.	WIRELESS INTERCOMS	OFFICE COMMUNICATIONS	TRANSMITS ROOM AUDIO OVER EXISTING POWER LINES TO RECEIVING DEVICE	SIZE: 3″ x 5″ x 10″ FREQUENCY: 100-200 KHz, RANGE: 50-300 FT	$25-$100	PRIVATE SECTOR	HOBBY AND MAIL ORDER
8.	TELEPHONE CONFERENCE CALL MONITORS	TELEPHONE CALL MONITORING	TRANSMITS TELEPHONE LINE ELECTRICAL SIGNALS TO DISTANT RADIO RECEIVER	SIZE: 1″ x 1″ x 1″ FREQUENCY: 88-108 MHz RANGE: 50-100 FT	$5-$20	PRIVATE SECTOR	HOBBY AND MAIL ORDER
9.	CARRIER CURRENT TRANSMITTER	ROOM MONITORING	USES VLF TO COMMUNICATE OVER EXISTING POWER LINES TO THE LISTENING POST.	SIZE: 1″ x 2″ x 2″ RANGE: 100-500 FT	$200-$400	GOVERN-MENT SECTOR	LAW EN-FORCEMENT SUPPLIERS
10.	MICROWAVE TRANSMITTER	ROOM MONITORING	USES MICROWAVE BEAM TO COMMUNICATE TO RECEIVING SITE	SIZE: 3″ x 2″ x 4″ RANGE: 200-1000 FT	$1000-$2000	GOVERN-MENT SECTOR	LAW EN-FORCEMENT SUPPLIERS
11.	PASSIVE REFLECTORS	ROOM MONITORING	REFLECTS INCOMING RADIO BEAM BACK TO SENDER WITH AUDIO SIGNALS ADDED	SIZE: 5″ x 1/2″ x 1/4″ RANGE: 500-1000 FT	$2000-$10,000	GOVERN-MENT SECTOR	LAW EN-FORCEMENT SUPPLIERS
12.	SWITCH RECEIVERS	REMOTE CONTROL OF EAVESDROPPING TRANSMITTERS	MINIATURE RADIO RE-CEIVER TURNS ON AND OFF POWER OF BUG TRANSMITTER BY REMOTE CONTROL	SIZE: 1″ x 3″ x 4″ RANGE: DEPENDENT ON ACTIVATOR POWER	$300-$1000	GOVERN-MENT SECTOR	LAW EN-FORCEMENT SUPPLIERS
13.	LIGHT BEAM (NON-COHERENT)	ROOM MONITORING	USES HIGHLY DIRECTIONAL LIGHT BEAM TO SEND AUDIO BETWEEN TWO POINTS	SIZE: 1′ x 3′ x 2′ RANGE: 1000 FT	$1000-$3000	NONE	LABORATORY AND ELECTRONIC EQUIPMENT SUPPLIERS
14.	LASERS (COHERENT)	ROOM MONITORING	USES LASER BEAM TO DETECT MINUTE VIBRATIONS	RANGE: UNKNOWN	$10,000-$50,000	NONE	LABORATORY AND ELECTRONIC EQUIPMENT SUPPLIERS
15.	MINIATURE TAPE RECORDERS	ROOM MONITORING AND EVIDENCE CORROBORATION	LEAVE BEHIND PACKAGE CONTAINS CONCEALED TAPE RECORDER	SIZE: 2 1/2″ x 5″ x 1 1/2″	$200-$7000	LIMITED USE IN ALL SECTORS	ELECTRONIC AND AUDIO EQUIPMENT SUPPLIERS

TABLE III

2.0 Audio Security Countermeasures

Audio countermeasures (ACM), technical security countermeasures, or simply "debugging" are terms used to describe the science of audio surveillance device detection and penetration prevention. This section examines the current status of audio countermeasures and describes the equipment available, its application, and limitations, and discusses the suitability of various devices for effective detection and protection against electronic invasions of privacy.

2.1 Telephone Systems

The telephone instrument and system are most important to the eavesdropper in that they provide numerous opportunities to gather audio information. As stated in Section 1.1, two basic types of devices exist, those which eavesdrop on the telephone conversation and those which utilize part of the telephone system for room eavesdropping. This section addresses the security countermeasures equipment used for each threat.

2.1.1 Telephone Taps. The telephone tap intercepts conventional telephone conversations as described in Section 1.1.1. This section describes countermeasures equipment and practices for each approach to telephone conversation eavesdropping.

2.1.1.1 Wire Systems. It should be emphasized at the outset that there are no existing ways to prove conclusively the existence or nonexistence of a telephone tap short of physically inspecting the telephone lines. Many of the ACM devices that are currently advertised represent attempts at tap detection which in some limited circumstances could determine the presence of a tap device if the tap is improperly installed or the tap device is of grossly inferior quality. The detection methodology used exploits the telephone system's normal switching functions by drawing current from the line when the instrument is not in use, or by simply measuring telephone line voltages. The devices which draw current from the telephone do so in such a way that, if any additional current were drawn by the attachment of a listening device or actuator switch, the total amount of current drawn would trigger the telephone company's switching exchange and cause the line to be continuously busy. Those devices which simply measure line voltage attempt to achieve the same result by detecting voltage changes caused by the attachment of listening or switch actuator devices. Neither of these methods provides any useful degree of security.

One of the problems presented in tap detection is that the target instrument may be located on the end of a very long line extending from a central station, passing through numerous cables, connected in terminal boxes, and finally entering a residence or an office. A telephone tap can be inserted anywhere between the central station and the target instrument. To check this maze of electrical wiring from the instrument end of this lengthy wire is usually more difficult than checking the system from the telephone switching station, where various currents and other line electrical characteristics can be readily measured. Unfortunately, the individual suspecting a wiretap is not always inclined to present this problem to the telephone company for analysis. When the telephone company does check telephone line pairs from the central station or from various points between the central station to the target instrument, certain unusual characteristics can indicate the presence of a non-professional tap.

One of the ACM devices widely offered for sale exploits characteristics of the telephone system to detect the insertion of taps, and the manufacturer claims that only illegal wiretaps will be located. Reputable manufacturers have checked this device and find its detection capabilities are virtually non-existent. The difficulties of tap detection primarily result from the characteristics of the telephone line itself, as the electrical characteristics of any given pair of telephone wires will change with variations in weather, humidity, temperature, lengths of line to the central station, and equipment additions within the system. These changes can be much greater in magnitude than the changes caused by the attachment of an efficient, high quality wiretap device.

A more sophisticated system sends pulses of energy down the telephone wires; these pulses are then reflected from electrical junctions along the wire back to the source. If a wiretap is inserted, it will appear as a new electrical junction. This approach is usable only in situations where a good history of the system installation is known since reflections from existing equipment would not indicate improper additions to the system. This technology is called time domain reflectometry and is too complex to be done by other than skilled personnel.

The only tap devices which are detectable are those attached to the telephone line which draw an excessive amount of current causing consequent change in the system voltage. Such tap devices can be detected with very simple equipment costing far less than some fraudulent tap detection systems being sold. For example, a $20 volt meter could provide the same level of confidence in tap detection as some equipment offered for sale for nearly $3,000. None of these ACM devices will detect the attachment of wires or voltage actuated switches which use matching networks, or which sense voltage changes between a single telephone wire and earth ground, or systems which are inductively coupled to the telephone line and are voice actuated. All of these techniques are possible telephone line surveillance practices.

There are only two recognized methods of telephone tap protection: the first requires discontinued use of the telephone instrument for the conveyance of secure information; the second is the use of quality audio scramblers. Neither protects against a tap; both are designed to protect against an interception of information. There are no scramblers available which will completely protect against a telephone tap; the only available systems merely make it more difficult for a tap to be successful. The scrambler disguises the audio signals that pass over the telephone lines by carefully mixing the signals in coded fashion at one end of the conversation and unmixing them at the other. It provides a measure of protection against hardwire and radio telephone tap systems.

Scrambler technology and prices vary widely. Pairs of scrambler devices may cost as little as $200 to $400 and are quite simple in their signal processing. These devices offer protection from less technically competent eavesdroppers and are perhaps effective for a short period of time against the eavesdropper who is equipped with some technical knowledge and laboratory equipment. Expensive scramblers cost several thousand dollars and use digitizing techniques, which can be quite effective. They may perform poorly over long distance lines because of limited channel band width and the time taken for the electrical signals to travel back and forth. They usually perform much better over radio communication links because propagation time is less of a factor. Currently there are no systems available which offer absolute security over conventional telephone lines, and only the special wide band systems used by government agencies are considered secure.

2.1.1.2 Radio Systems. Electronic detection of a telephone tap transmitter installed on the target premises is much the same as detection of any other radio transmitter eavesdropping device. The only difference in the devices is that the audio signal is supplied by the telephone line instead of by room conversation. The radio tap devices, however, have one major advantage over room transmitters in that they need not be installed near the premises where the target instrument is located and may be attached to the telephone line at any accessible point. Therefore, chances of discovery by either physical search or radio spectrum search may be limited. Location of the installation is the principal difference between effectively detecting a radio

telephone tap and a radio room bug by the means described in Section 2.2. Several characteristics should be mentioned however, which make radio telephone tap detection unique.

Since the telephone tap transmitter is designed exclusively for the intercept of the telephone conversation, as a general rule the telephone must be in use before any radio spectrum analysis can begin. This is achieved by placing the instrument in operation by calling a cooperative telephone and conversing in a non-alerting manner. The telephone transmitter should be activated by this process unless a remote switch receiver is being used and is deactivated at this time. If this is the case, only physical inspection will discover the tap. It should be noted that an r-f search will not be effective unless the transmitter is within the operating range of the detecting device. One r-f signal strength tap detection device is available which works well if the tap transmitter is inside the telephone instrument. This device, if placed adjacent to the telephone, should indicate the presence of a drop-in mouthpiece or any other operating transmitter installed in the instrument. The use of this field strength measuring device for telephone radio tap checking is possible since the instrument can be identified as the single source of radiation. A brief visual inspection of the suspect instrument can provide similar results. Additional discussion of field strength devices to locate room bugs is presented in Section 2.2.

There are very few practices which can protect against r-f telephone tap devices. The only device offered on the commercial market is an r-f jammer, which is illegal under FCC regulations in this country. Another method is the employment of shielded rooms, provided that the transmitter is located within the shielded area. Each of these methods are discussed in Section 2.3.

One manufacturer claims that if a device were connected to the telephone line pair at the target telephone that could raise and lower the telephone line voltage at a slow rate, perhaps four or five times a second, radio eavesdropping devices which use the telephone line for a power supply would be upset and possibly suffer a momentary frequency change in their transmission. In the listening post this sudden change of frequency would cause momentary loss of audio in the eavesdropper's radio receiver.

2.1.2 Telephone Room Eavesdropping Devices. Each of the telephone system eavesdropping devices discussed in Section 1.1.2 may be detected through the use of various electronic technologies or their effectiveness reduced by use of specific electronic protective devices and procedures. The following sections address these countermeasures devices and procedures.

2.1.2.1. Infinity Transmitters, Listen-Backs, and Keep-Alives. The detection of an active infinity transmitter is relatively easy, but the intentional activation of a quiescent device by a sweep team is not easy. Several manufacturers offer countermeasures systems which are designed for direct attachment to the suspect telephones lines. These systems emit variable frequency tones that sweep the audio spectrum in an attempt to trigger the implanted surveillance device. In newer infinity devices available on the European market, the simultaneous presence of different tones, or time-spaced tones, is required to activate the transmitter. The currently available tone activation countermeasures devices do not affect these multiple tone units; however a few manufacturers, aware of the multi-tone requirement, may soon produce multi-tone sweeping units. Though tone sweeping is designed to trigger the infinity device, actual detection is accomplished by determining that the device has responded by electronically picking up the telephone. For example, the tone sweeping generator is connected directly to the telephone wires through a matching network, and the telephone instrument is left on-hook causing the line voltages to remain at the normal 48 volt level. Then, if the generator produces the proper triggering tone or tones and activates the infinity transmitter, the line voltage drops to between 6 and 12 volts, a change which is easily measured with a conventional voltmeter. As an alternative, if the target phone is dialed from a remote location and the proper tones are placed on the line through the mouthpiece of this instrument, the telephone at the target will stop ringing and room audio may be heard. If the telephone continues to ring, the infinity device is either not present or has not activated. Equipment that places audio tones on a telephone line is available for $130 to $150. The more costly telephone instrument inspection systems frequently contain audio tone generators in addition to the equipment required for complete instrument analysis. Other inexpensive devices are available which monitor voltage levels only. These connect directly across the suspect telephone lines and do not activate the infinity device. They merely monitor the voltage level on the line and, should an infinity device be activated while the telephone is in the on-hook position, the change in line voltage is immediately detected. These devices are especially applicable for use on single line telephones where there is no lighted push-button to indicate telephone line use. They are usually priced between $90 and $130 and require installation over long periods of time to increase the probability of detection, and should be used continuously to attain a high level of confidence.

The detection of listen-back or keep-alive devices requires either telephone line voltage monitoring or audio detection equipment. When the eavesdropper dials the target telephone from a remote location and the target instrument is answered and then hung up, the keep-alive device keeps the telephone line open, permitting the eavesdropper to overhear room audio. Tones do not activate this device, but it can be easily detected by calling the target telephone and duplicating this procedure. The line voltage monitor unit already described can indicate that a listen-back device is in use since the line voltage generally remains below 12 volts after the instrument is hung up when it should be approximately 48 volts.

2.1.2.2 On-Line Microphones. As described in section 1.1.2.3, microphone devices which monitor room conversations can use telephone lines for short range transmission of the audio from the target area to the listening post. They may be electronically detected, while operating, only through the use of an audio amplifier connected across the telephone lines being used. However, because audio signals may be transmitted over any suitable pair of wires, detecting these devices becomes more difficult in the case of the multiline instruments with their fifty line cables. Considering the redundant wires, ground wires, and signal wires, there are 1225 possible line pairs available to pass audio. To monitor all of these combinations is cumbersome and inconclusive. If the on-line microphone incorporates some voltage switch activating technique, room audio would not necessarily be present at any given time, nor would the switching element be easily stimulated, because of the vast number of possible activation signals. No manufacturers are known to supply telephone line voltage stimulation equipment designed to activate devices of this nature primarily because of the potential damage they might cause to the telephone system itself as a result of the various applied voltages.

2.1.2.3 Telephone Modification. The basic electronic tool used to check for telephone modifications is the telephone analyzer or checker. This piece of equipment allows the operator to select two individual wires in any combination from a large number of wires in the 4 to 50 wire cable bundles which extend from the base of the standard telephone. The operator generally disconnects the cable at a convenient junction point, usually at the wall connector block, and attaches the end extending from the instrument to the analysis equipment, leaving the other cable end free and unconnected.

After the attachment is made to the telephone analyzer, the operator systematically selects each possible pair combination and tests the pair to determine its electrical characteristics. In the case of the 50 wire cable, there are 1225 practical combinations to check. If an internal electronic modification exists, the characteristics of the specific altered line pair should become immediately apparent. In order to activate a device which needs some form of electrical stimulation to operate, most telephone analyzers usually contain tone generators, and audio amplifiers. These tests of the instrument are to detect internal modifications only and have nothing to do with locating a tap unless a radio tap device has been installed across the talk pair in the instrument.

Several manufacturers offer analyzers which are designed to attach not only to the isolated instrument for electrical analysis, but also to the outgoing telephone lines. In this test, the analyzer usually performs three functions. It accurately measures line voltages and current drain under both on- and off-hook conditions; stimulates the line with audio tones in an attempt to activate infinity devices; and monitors for audio which could be present from various on-line microphone devices. Some analyzers have one added test, that of checking for r-f carrier current transmitters. While operating in this mode, the analyzers usually do not perform high voltage stimulation tests because doing so could damage telephone company property and electronic equipment. Care must be taken in the operation of any line analysis equipment to avoid the infusion of noise into the telephone company system or upsetting system performance.

Even though some telephone analyzers may be automated, a great deal of skill and understanding of the telephone system is required for proper analyzer operation and interpretation of results. The automated analyzers offered on the commercial market tend to be expensive, ranging from $1500 to $8000 depending on the number of wires tested and the types of line tests performed. The proper use of telephone analyzers frequently requires twenty minutes to an hour to inspect a single five-button telephone instrument, even if one of the automated systems is used. These costly systems electronically select and cycle through each wire pair combination to locate internal, instrument modifying components. The existence of these components may not be apparent during a visual inspection.

The protection systems offered to the private sector which are designed to offset the threat of telephone modification or compromise fall into two categories. One system physically disconnects the telephone instrument from the outgoing wires and thereby prevents the passage of audio from the instrument onto the wires; a second system injects a jamming signal into the instrument which masks audio by burying it deep in noise. In this latter concept the noise itself does not go onto the telephone wires, but is contained within the instrument and it is equally effective on single-line and multi-line instruments.

The basic telephone disconnect system is the plug-and-jack type found in residential extension telephones. This is simply a plug on the end of a single line instrument cable which is plugged into a receptacle when the telephone is in use and is disconnected when the instrument is not in use. The only requirement for use of this system is the installation of an external ringer to signal an incoming call. These disconnect systems have been found to be inadequate because the user frequently is not inclined to plug and unplug the instrument each time the telephone is used.

Basically, the isolation of the telephone instrument from the wires exiting a room prevents the use of many telephone modification techniques of room audio intercept. Telephone line disconnects do not, however, protect against self-powered transmitters installed in the telephone instrument. More sophisticated instrument isolators use fiber optics to pass standard audio signals and restrict the passage of unauthorized signals to the outside wires. The cost of these devices is prohibitive, but they were found to be available during this study; none was determined to be in use except on an experimental basis.

There are some operational techniques which can be used by the security conscious individual to inhibit successful telephone modification penetration. The first applies to the standard five-button or multi-line office instrument. If all the buttons are returned to the up position while the telephone is not in use, the threat of compromise is reduced because one half of the internal electrical connections necessary for the eavesdropper to perform the eavesdropping cease to exist. This occurs because the telephone instrument's internal design causes a portion of the hook-switch to be connected when one button is depressed. Left in this position, the eavesdropper must only complete the remaining hook-switch by-pass to accomplish an operational compromise.

2.2 Radio Eavesdropping Device Detection

The detection of radio transmitter devices requires the use of fairly sophisticated electronic countermeasures equipment. This section provides a brief overview of the devices available to the public which afford this capability in varying degrees.

2.2.1 Field Strength Measurement. The field strength meter is a device designed to measure the relative radio frequency energy which is present at some point in space. This broad band device indicates the cumulative total of the power present from all sources throughout a major portion of the radio spectrum. The field strength measuring device contains an antenna, a diode detector, and a sensitive amplifier which drives a meter or other circuitry to provide an indication of the relative r-f energy intensity detected. This measurement is usually displayed on a meter but may also be represented by an audio response or a simple indicator light. Fabrication of a field strength meter by a technician is possible for an investment of less than $50 in parts.

The basic field strength measurement device has been refined and made sophisticated. In some cases controls are added to allow the operator to normalize or null the meter to the local environment as in a region of high r-f background energy, such as in the middle of a city. This concentrated energy would saturate the detector and indicate a continuous "active" condition. Other refinements include the addition of limited tuning capability in which one wide band is broken into small segments to permit discrete amplification of the energy within a particular frequency segment. Frequently, the output of the field strength meter is amplified to a high level to operate a speaker contained within the unit. If the device is placed in the vicinity of an operating radio transmitter microphone which is using FM or AM modulation and the transmitter is of sufficient power, there is potential for creating a feedback "squeal" between the transmitter and the speaker in the field strength unit. This detection method, although not necessarily conclusive, could be highly alerting to a potential eavesdropper and is generally not good practice if further efforts are planned to locate the listening post as well as the device.

An alternate of this feature requires the field strength meter output to be demodulated so that the operator can monitor the audio of the transmitted signal in a non-alerting manner to determine the presence of a clandestine transmitter. As field strength measurement techniques have become more sophisticated, single packages are available that contain two field strength measurement circuits and use dual antennae operating in a differential mode. The principle of operation used in this device takes into consideration antennae placement and differential energy measurement. One antenna, being closer to the surveillance transmitter than the other, will receive a different amount of energy than is detected from the other antenna. The difference in energy or signal strength at each antenna occurs only if one antenna is closer to an operating transmitter than the other. This tends to reduce the effects of distant, high power, commercial transmitters, since the field strength appearing at both antennae would appear essentially the same.

All of the field strength measurement "debugging" devices reviewed during the study are combinations of the foregoing options, each option providing somewhat different capabilities. All devices suffer the basic disadvantages of broad band diode detection; (refer to Figure 12.). The diode detector, field strength meter, or crystal detector, all synonyms for the same device, has limited application in the practice of countermeasures inspections. It should not be relied upon as the principal means of radio transmitter detection. These devices are relatively inexpensive, costing from $20 to $300 depending on the options offered and the quality of manufacture. Limitations of these devices include broad spectrum width with corresponding large variations in sensitivity, poor selectivity, inability to detect carrier current devices, and susceptibility to standing wave reflections which may occur inside buildings.

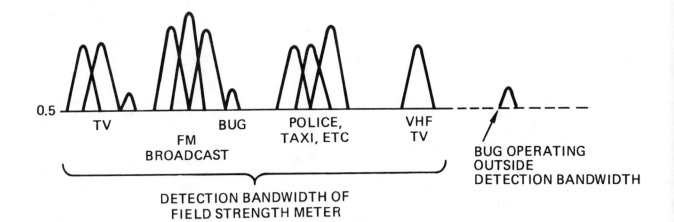

0.5

TV

FM
BROADCAST

BUG

POLICE,
TAXI, ETC

VHF
TV

BUG OPERATING
OUTSIDE
DETECTION BANDWIDTH

DETECTION BANDWIDTH OF
FIELD STRENGTH METER

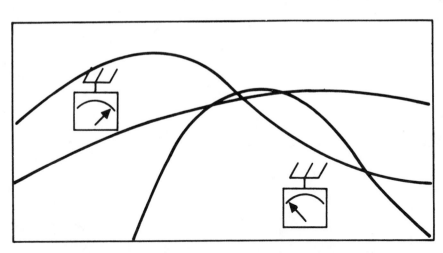

FIELD STRENGTH MAY VARY ACROSS A ROOM
DUE TO STANDING WAVE REFLECTIONS

FIGURE 12. FIELD STRENGTH METER "BUG" DETECTORS

The field strength measurement device is usually unable to detect low power eavesdropping devices which are transmitting in high r-f energy backgrounds or devices operating near the frequencies of large, high-powered commercial broadcast transmitters. This inability to locate r-f transmitters in high noise background environments significantly reduces effectiveness. The field strength meter, however, does have a place in countermeasures as a secondary or back-up probe in r-f detection.

2.2.2 Countermeasures Receivers. The major and important difference between countermeasures receivers and those receivers commonly used for commercial broadcast reception is that the countermeasures device is designed to search a large portion of the r-f spectrum, isolate and identify a signal, and demodulate this signal to ascertain its nature and information content. It is often erroneously assumed that clandestine eavesdropping devices most likely operate between 88 MHz and 108 MHz, the commercial FM broadcast band. Instead, it should be assumed that the entire spectrum is available to the eavesdropper and can be used with the application of available technology.

Requisite technical characteristics of surveillance or countermeasures receivers demonstrate high sensitivity and selectivity over the large radio spectrum, are capable of many different demodulation techniques, exhibit frequency stability and capability to acquire weak signals, and demonstrate high rejection of unwanted signals in adjacent frequency ranges. None of these capabilities is normally provided in receivers other than counter surveillance receivers. The frequency range of the receivers should at least cover the operating range of presently available transistors whose price allows them to be used for fabrication of surveillance transmitters. Frequently an FM broadcast receiver is used as a countermeasures receiver, but it is limited not only in frequency range but also in ability to detect low level signals and sub-carrier signals which require a greater band width and additional demodulation capabilities. As shown in Figure 13, the commercial receiver band width is not wide enough to allow reception of sub-carrier transmissions. This illustration is a visual display that may be added to the countermeasures receiver and is called a "pan adaptor". It provides a picture of many radio transmitters' signals and their relative strength in the portion of the radio spectrum being analyzed.

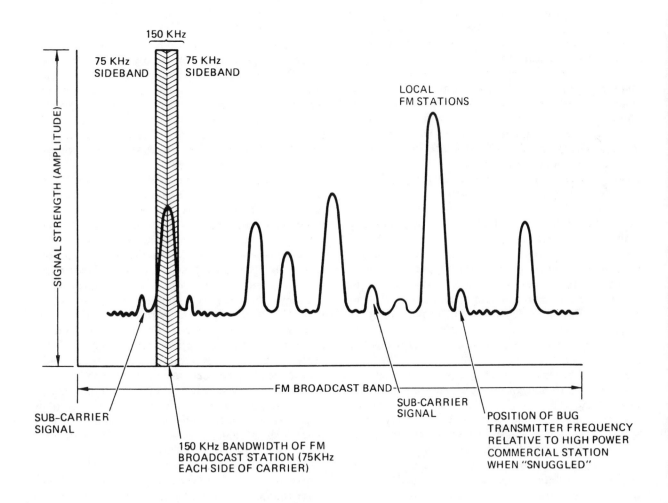

FIGURE 13. FM BROADCAST BAND SPECTRUM

49

Usually the automatic frequency control (AFC) of commercial FM receivers prevents them from being tuned to a low power signal such as that transmitted by a surveillance transmitter because the receiver will automatically lock on any adjacent signal from a high power, commercial broadcast station.[14] (Recall the practice of snuggling or of placing a low power, clandestine transmission adjacent to a high power broadcast signal.) One other drawback to the use of commercial FM receivers regards that inherent inability to cover their own Intermediate Frequency (IF), usually 10.7 MHz. The design of these receivers precludes their operation near these frequencies and the skilled eavesdropper can fabricate devices that operate near this frequency range. Likewise, the wireless microphone designed to operate in the FM region can be tuned outside this frequency band.

The quality countermeasures receiver may be manually tuned or computer controlled for automatic cycling through the spectrum.[15] Systems of this nature are available on the commercial market but their prices range from $50,000 to over $100,000, depending on the characteristics desired, such as frequency ranges involved, types of modulation, and extent of automatic processing.

A few manufacturers produce quality portable equipment. These receivers are quite popular and cost between $6,000 and $11,000. They generally satisfy the requirements of providing broad frequency coverage and various demodulation techniques, including FM, AM, upper and lower single side band, and narrow band FM. In addition, band widths are frequently adjustable from 1 KHz to 10 MHz. Better quality units will provide a signal display capability on a pan adaptor. This last feature is considered a necessity since it provides the operator with the ability to assess visually the sophisticated modulation techniques, the presence of subcarriers and snuggle devices, and improves the general flexibility and usefulness of the entire system. These surveillance receivers are fully capable of locating and identifying any of the transmitters described in the first chapter of this report with the exception of those which cannot be detected due to a specific frequency being used that is beyond the range of the receiver or because remotely activated transmitters are in the "off" mode.

The only unconventional modulation technique used in radio surveillance devices which are available to the law enforcement sector is the sub-carrier technique described in section 1.3.2.4. These sub-carrier transmitter signals are not detectable by conventional radio receivers; they are not easily demodulated.[16] They may be visually detected, however, with a spectrum analyzer or countermeasures receiver with a panoramic display attachment. In the latter case the receiver intercepts and visually displays the energy of the device on a small video screen, though it is not possible to retrieve the original audio signal without additional processing. As described in 1.3.2.4, two receiver detection processes are required to reproduce the desired audio. The first receiver detects the principal high frequency signal. In the next step, a second receiver processes the low frequency sub-carrier signal to reproduce the original audio. To systematically test each suspect radio signal for sub-carrier modulation during a countermeasures radio spectrum analysis, this same dual detection process must be completed. It is obvious that this activity can be extremely expensive and time consuming where a large number of radio signals is involved. For this reason some manufacturers offer crude sub-carrier detectors in small easy to use packages which are designed for use with another primary receiving device. These sub-carrier detectors, however, lack signal selectivity and sensitivity and, therefore, may easily overlook the lower powered clandestine sub-carrier device.

If the principal frequency of a sub-carrier transmitter is received on a single conventional receiver and no provisions are made for the second processing step, the audio output of the receiver will appear muted or silent since the sub-carrier signal frequency is far above the audio detection range. To gain added security, the eavesdropper may then select a major operating frequency which is exactly the same as a commercial broadcast station. This won't affect the performance at the sub-carrier transmitter because the sub-carrier signal is far outside the detection band width of the receiver; however, now rather than a muted audio output being produced at the receiver's speaker, the normal audio carried by the commercial broadcast station will be heard. In this manner, the basic characteristics of the sub-carrier transmitter can be used to significantly increase its secrecy since even the existence of the main carrier can be concealed.

One possible future threat regards the use of clandestine video and data devices which transmit other than oral data. Not only are these devices not restricted by current laws, but their detection and demodulation can be extremely difficult without appropriate knowledge of the signal and the use of costly analysis equipment.

The surveillance receiver is a tool which must be utilized with skill equal to that of the eavesdropper. The counter surveillance expert must apply this tool in situations to detect devices that are most attractive to the opponent. For example, sweeping with receivers has no effect on the remotely switched devices which transmit data at a different time than during the sweeping. Likewise, sweeping cannot detect passive devices unless they are active during the time of the inspection. These devices must be found through physical search or X-ray analysis. The detection of microwave links is also impossible without the use of special antennae placed in a position to receive the transmitted energy. An additional consideration often overlooked by users of surveillance receivers is that of the normal receiver whip antenna. The single fixed length antenna commonly used over the 30 MHz to 1000 MHz frequency range will show repeated and predictable nulls in its ability to receive specific frequencies. This effect is caused by the fixed geometric relationship between the physical length of the antenna and the wave length of a specific radio frequency. If this relationship is improper, the energy level of the specific frequency being received will be reduced, thereby making it possible for the radio receiver to overlook the signal because of its apparently small signal strength. Suitable antenna systems which can overcome much of this lack of performance are available at prices up to $2000. However, one skilled in the art of countermeasures can manipulate antenna lengths and the placement of receivers during the sweep to overcome many of these deficiencies.

Another use of the low frequency counter surveillance receiver is in the detection of the VLF carrier current transmitters.[17] Detection of VLF transmitters is generally not possible by anything but a VLF receiver which should have good sensitivity to detect the low power signals, and exhibit good selectivity. (These receivers are also used in the second demodulation process for the detection of sub-carrier signals.) This level of performance cannot be achieved with the less expensive devices offered by commercial product manufacturers. Those offered for sale can only detect higher powered, carrier current devices within limited ranges. These counter surveillance VLF receivers are connected directly to the power lines or telephone lines with special voltage isolation adaptors to prevent high voltages from damaging the receiver or injuring the operator. The low frequency spectrum is scanned in much the same fashion as with the higher frequency countermeasures receivers. It should be re-emphasized that the carrier current transmitter radiates very little r-f energy into space and is therefore not detectable without a direct connection to the lines being examined. The range of transmitters utilizing this technique is frequently underestimated. One manufacturer experimented with carrier current devices and was able to retrieve an audio signal three blocks from the site of signal initiation after circumventing two power line transformers, commonly claimed to filter and prevent transmissions of this sort. In this case, the transformers were provided with bypasses by the power company to enable it to use carrier current controlled equipment.

2.2.3 Spectrum Analysis. In recent years the spectrum analyzer has gained an accepted place in the countermeasures electronic field due to its flexibility and capabilities for visual display of sophisticated modulation processes.[18] Typically, the analyzer exhibits less sensitivity than the countermeasures receiver; however, this disadvantage in some instances is offset by the ability to display a large portion of the radio spectrum and the corresponding side bands that may contain audio signal information. Newer spectrum analyzers have provisions for varying the band width and displaying the spectrum to allow uncluttered reception of transmissions. Until recently, spectrum analyzers tended to be large and unwieldy. In the last few years small, portable units have been developed and now are available to the countermeasures technician. Properly used, the spectrum analyzer can be used for analysis of signals throughout the radio spectrum and with additional attachments, can be used to analyze audio signals and carrier current signals in a manner that is not possible with a countermeasures receiver or audio amplifier.

The spectrum analyzer does have certain limitations.[19] Its reduced sensitivity requires that it be in proximity to the surveillance device for detection. Once a device is detected, most spectrum analyzers do not provide a demodulated output. The cost of these devices is relatively high, running from $3,000 to $7,000 depending on the included accessories, frequency ranges, and portability. Professional organizations use the analyzer to augment the surveillance receiver, to identify those signals not detectable by the receiver, and to provide assistance in analysis through visual presentation. Figure 14 illustrates the ability of the spectrum analyzer to display larger segments of the radio spectrum than the radio receiver. Figures 15 and 16[20] illustrate the relative costs and performance levels of the several r-f detection methods and devices described.

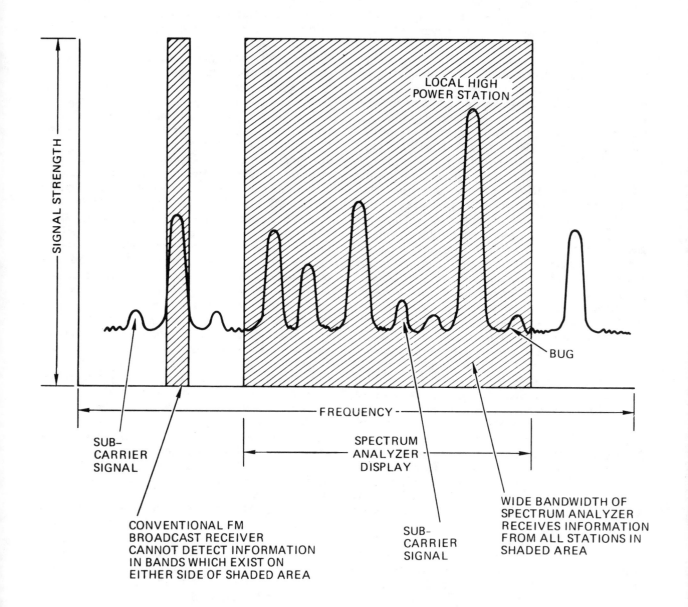

FIGURE 14. RADIO SPECTRUM DISPLAY

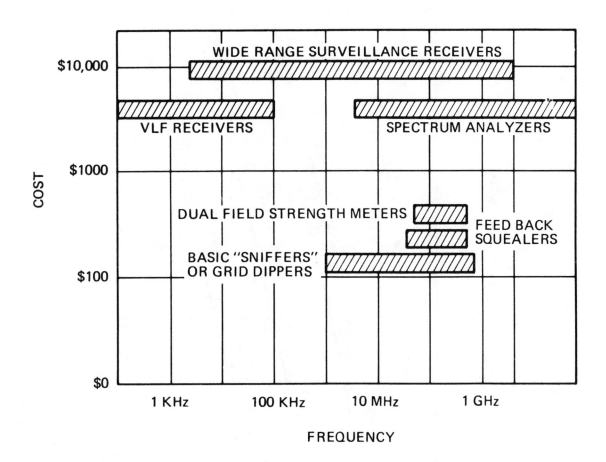

**FIGURE 15. COST VERSUS FREQUENCY COVERAGE
OF RADIO DETECTION DEVICES**

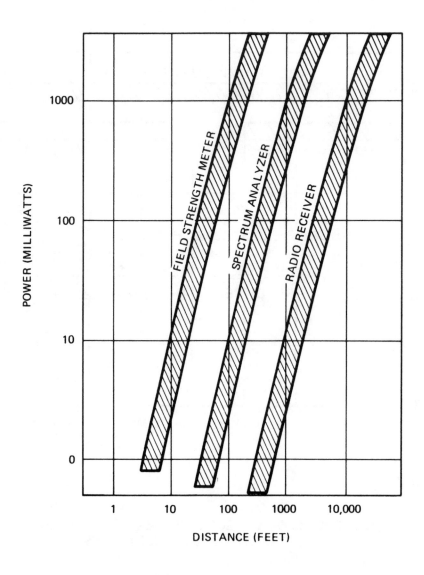

FIGURE 16. RADIO DEVICES TRANSMITTING POWER VS. EFFECTIVE RANGE

2.2.4 Other Inspection Equipment. This section offers a brief description of other detection systems that are available to the countermeasures expert and represent additions to a basic equipment list. All of the technologies employed by these devices have been demonstrated in the private sector and provide increasing thoroughness to the countermeasures detection process.

For example, portable X-rays have been used for years.[21] These units utilize either direct visual display on flourescent screens or photography. X-ray analysis of most objects provides conclusive evidence of the product integrity. Complex pictures of radios, telephones and other electronic devices, however, require detailed study by experts. X-ray systems are available that weigh twenty to forty pounds and cost between $1000 and $3000.

The detection of optical links, including infrared and laser systems, requires the use of photo detectors. Systems of this type designed specifically for the detection of clandestine optical links are not available.

Metal detectors[22] fall in the same category as field strength measurement devices but are used by the countermeasures expert who limits their use to inspection of completely non-metallic objects such as wooden furniture, foam cushions, or ceramic ashtrays. They have little value when used on walls, floors, ceiling and other structural members, as those areas are likely to contain nails, reinforcing bars, pieces of wire, metallic trash, and plumbing. The technologies of metal detection, the specific capabilities, sensitivities, and ranges are not reviewed here. Good detectors are available to the public, the less sophisticated costing as little as $50, and more capable laboratory analysis and magnetic measurement devices costing over several thousand dollars.[23]

No sweep team is complete without possession of the necessary audio amplifiers, earphones, and hand tools including various meters, pliers, wirecutters, spatulas for prying away wallboard, tweezers, and rubber hammers. All of these tools are used to assist in physical inspection as well as electrical analysis of suspect fixtures, devices and wires. The monetary investment is modest for a complete accessory kit and may be less than $150.

2.3 General Purpose Audio Surveillance Protection Systems

Such a protection system assumes that a device may be present and attempts to negate its effectiveness. The following descriptions are applicable to most radio bugging devices without regard to their frequencies, modulation, or physical characteristics.

2.3.1 Acoustic Protection. The basic acoustic protection system is a specially designed room within a room.[24] Sensitive meetings may be held within this structure, and participants can be relatively confident of conversation security.

A common fallacy is that audio noise generation, such as a background radio playing in the room where sensitive conversations are held, provides good audio security by covering the conversation. This practice provides only a modest level of security, however, since this noise tends to be musical in nature and some of it can be filtered from conversation recordings because of its different frequency characteristics. Further ineffectiveness is caused by reducing the volume of the radio to the level which can only be considered background noise; if the radio volume is increased, the conversationalists merely increase the volume of their communication as well, thereby defeating the purpose of the whole arrangement. One improvement is the use of noise sources that contain audio energy distributed evenly throughout the frequency region of human speech. These audio sources include running water, flushing toilets, gurgling fish tanks, window fans, and phonograph records. Sounds of this nature provide the type of masking that can significantly reduce the interpretability of an intercepted conversation. The use of these technologies is widely known in all sectors. However, misunderstanding of noise effectiveness as a countermeasures technique is quite apparent in the private sector. Devices which provide this masking are available commercially from a limited number of suppliers at nominal cost.

2.3.2 Radio Frequency Protection Systems. Rooms similar to those described in the previous section exist that protect against radio transmissions. These rooms are commonly known as r-f shielded rooms or screen rooms and are used extensively by electronic firms to provide r-f free environments for laboratory tests and analyses.

Commonly known r-f protection devices are the hash generators or radio frequency jammers, [25] which have existed since the Model-T spark coil. The r-f hash generators are prohibited by FCC regulation in this country but are not prohibited in many other areas of the world. The r-f generator supposedly renders a radio surveillance device ineffective by generating a high level of random noise or static throughout the spectrum in which the device may operate. Several inadequacies of this concept exist because the amount of energy necessary to reliably jam a small surveillance transmitter can be enormous. Consequently, this hash generation also interferes with local radio and television sets and the two-way communications of aircraft, police, and emergency vehicles operating in the vicinity. Devices of this nature are sold overseas and do occasionally find their way into this country. Those identified during the study generate very low r-f power, provide limited spectrum coverage, and are little more effective than a bad florescent light.

The only devices available for protection against carrier current devices on both telephone lines and power lines are absorptive line filters. These filters prevent the passage over wires of frequencies above the audio range and severely attenuate the normally used carrier current spectrum between 20 KHz and 500 KHz. Power line filters tend to be bulky because of power handling requirements, and such a device for each power line may be 2 to 3 feet in length and 4 or more inches in diameter. Those suitable for use on telephone lines are significantly smaller. Carrier current power line filters are readily available and are frequently used in conjunction with r-f shielded rooms. In a security application these filters are placed on the lines exiting the secure area and require proper installation and grounding. These filters cost $500 to $1,000 each depending on power handling requirements of the secure area.

Active jamming of surveillance tape recorders has been rumored in various publications, and this phenomenon does exist in limited situations. Theoretically, a 60 KHz signal is injected into a telephone or other suspect wire and, if these lines are connected to a susceptible tape recorder, this 60 KHz signal can upset the recording system and reduce the quality of the recorded conversation. Use of this technology for security purposes is more the exception than the rule since the susceptibility of recording systems to this type of jamming varies widely. Signals of this frequency are occasionally used for tape erasing, but they do not travel far along a telephone line or maintain sufficient strength to have a significant effect upon a properly connected tape recording system.

2.4 Audio Countermeasures Services

The countermeasures sweep, or "debugging" as it is known in nonprofessional circles, is a systematic procedure designed to locate audio surveillance devices or attempts at audio penetration. In the past few years service organizations engaged in this practice have received notoriety and some have prospered through the sale of legitimate services. Even more have prospered through the sale of services of limited value which do little more than degrade the overall posture of security and instill a false sense of confidence. Even the services of legitimate organizations may be of limited value if their operation is poorly timed and not programmed to include a continuing security program.

As technology has progressed, the probability of a sweep team examining a target area and locating a clandestine device is relatively small; it is negligible if the team performing the service simply waves a field strength measurement device about, checks the furniture cushions, and pops the cover from the telephone. This section discusses the kind of countermeasures service organizations identified during this study; it also discusses those organizations that serve the service organizations by training individuals in the art of "debugging".

Security inspection organizations offer services using a variety of electronic equipment for a variety of costs. Frequently a countermeasures sweep is priced on the basis of square footage of the area to be examined, the types and number of telephones, or the number of man hours that must be expended to complete the task. The price per room charged in the private sector ranges from 10 cents to $1.00 per square foot. The organization that charges 10 cents per square foot typically uses a modified commercial radio receiver as the primary countermeasures tool, whereas the organization that charges $1.00 per square foot uses a wide band detector and a telephone analyzer. The latter organization cautions customers by suggesting that the information to be protected should be worth in excess of $100,000 or the service charge is not worth the investment. The organization offering the sweep service for 10 cents per square foot charged $17, $22, and $30 for single line telephone, five-button telephone, and call director examination, respectively, and the more expensive service firm quoted these same functional inspections at $25, $50 and $100 respectively. The charge, therefore, for sweeping a 10 x 15 foot office space with one five-button instrument ranges between $37 and $200. If priced on the man-hour basis of $50 per man hour, the minimum charge is $250. One company suggests that the breakdown of effort on a per room basis may be one hour of physical search, 30 to 45 minutes examination per telephone instrument, and two hours of radio spectrum monitoring to conduct the room sweep task. The reason for disparity among prices of service companies has become readily apparent. There is no countermeasures industry standardization of performance requirements, no specification of equipment utilized in sweep work, no accountability in hours spent to perform services, and no measure of competence of the sweep technicians. The prices do not correspond to quality of rendered services in this industry and, unfortunately, the consumer has no standard for comparison. Truly, the cost and effectiveness of countermeasures services appear to be solely related to the service organization's interpretation of what the market will bear.

One "sweep artist" was privileged with an extensive article a few years ago in the Wall Street Journal. This "expert" used a gray box with a red and green light as a bug detector. It was reported that during the sweep the red light was lit signifying that a bug was present. The technician claimed triumphantly to the customer that "the Feds had him bugged". The technician recommended that rather than finding the bug the customer call an associate and say in a loud voice over the telephone that he knew "the Feds had him bugged". The customer followed this procedure and a week later recalled the technician for an additional check of the premises. Predictably, the red light did not light and the technician claimed another successful debugging operation for a satisfied customer. The same debugger also used the scheme of "killing" the bug by flipping the switch of the gray box to change the red light to a green light while observing in a summary statement, "red you're dead; green, you're clean".[26]

During the course of this study six qualified organizations were identified that can competently provide countermeasures services. However, none of these firms provides a service which considers all of the possible surveillance techniques. This is not to say that in any given situation the potential of an audio penetration exists simply because it is possible, but a competent service organization should inform the client of equipment limitations and discuss services that are either necessary or unwarranted. In the private sector the services offered by these few companies were found to be adequate and priced fairly. The licensing of countermeasures service organizations is one recommendation contained in this report; licensing will assist the unwitting consumer in obtaining the proper dollar value for countermeasures services.

The level of competence available and quality of training offered by the organizations reviewed during this effort vary widely. The leading training organization is the U.S. government and the various intelligence agencies that hire engineers and train them over a period of years to possess a high degree of expertise. Corporations recruit retired federal agents and capitalize on this experience.

One private organization interviewed offers programs that are limited by the non-technical background of the trainees, and somewhat dated technology is presented by the instructors. Another organization located in the Southeast is well financed and displays a sophisticated public relations approach to training. This organization offers little in-depth quality to the trainees and capitalizes on current public interests in electronic intelligence activities. Another organization advertises openly in newspapers and offers to train "individuals with no technical experience". It reminds potential trainees of the "high profits" that can be made in the "debugging business". (This company also offers equipment that "permanently cancels out illegal bugs and telephone taps.") This type organization has received little scrutiny or restriction under state or federal statutes.

2.5 Summary of Audio Countermeasures Devices

The following table is a summary of audio countermeasures devices.

AUDIO COUNTERMEASURES EQUIPMENT

EQUIPMENT CATEGORY	APPLICATION	OPERATING PRINCIPLE	COST	EFFECTIVENESS
1. WIRE TAP DETECTORS	DETERMINE EXISTENCE OF TELEPHONE LINE TAP	MONITORS TELEPHONE LINE VOLTAGE FOR CHANGE	$20–$3000	LITTLE OR NONE
2. RADIO TAP DETECTORS	DETERMINE EXISTENCE OF RADIO TRANSMITTER WITHIN TELEPHONE	SENSES FIELD STRENGTH NEAR TELEPHONE	$150–$250	MAY DETERMINE PRESENCE OF OPERATING RADIO TRANSMITTER WITHIN TELEPHONE INSTRUMENT
3. INFINITY TRANSMITTER DETECTOR	DETERMINES EXISTENCE OF ACTIVE INFINITY TRANSMITTER	MONITORS TELEPHONE LINE VOLTAGE FOR CHANGE	$150–$250	WILL CONFIRM EXISTENCE OF ACTIVE INFINITY DEVICE
4. INFINITY TRANSMITTER ACTIVATOR	ACTIVATES INFINITY TRANSMITTER	PLACES AUDIO TONES ON TELEPHONE LINE	$150–$250	SHOULD ACTIVATE MANY SINGLE-TONE DEVICES, FEW MULTI-TONE DEVICES
5. TELEPHONE ANALYZERS	LOCATE TELEPHONE MODIFICATIONS	CHECK AND VERIFICATION OF TELEPHONE INSTRUMENT'S INTERNAL WIRING	$500–$6500	SHOULD LOCATE MANY TELEPHONE MODIFICATIONS
6. TELEPHONE LINE DISCONNECTS	PROTECT AGAINST TELE-PHONE MODIFICATIONS	ELECTRONICALLY SEPARATES UNUSED TELEPHONE INSTRU-MENT FROM OUTGOING LINES	$10–$600	GOOD PROTECTION AGAINST TELEPHONE MODIFICATION
7. FIELD STRENGTH DETECTORS, "SNIFFERS", AND "SQUEALERS"	LOCATE OPERATING RADIO TRANSMITTER BUGS	SENSES RADIO ENERGY OVER PORTION OF THE RADIO SPECTRUM IN A LOCAL AREA	$200–$500	SOME DETECTION CAPABILITY IF PROPERLY USED
8. COUNTERMEASURES RADIO RECEIVERS	DETECT OPERATING RADIO TRANSMITTER BUGS	SENSE SPECIFIC RADIO FRE-QUENCIES WHEN TUNED OVER LARGE PORTION OF RADIO SPECTRUM	$1500–$8000	GOOD DETECTION OF MOST OPERATIONAL RADIO DEVICES
9. SPECTRUM ANALYZERS	DETECT OPERATING RADIO TRANSMITTER BUGS, SIGNAL ANALYSIS	SENSES AND DISPLAYS SELECTED BROAD SECTIONS OF RADIO SPECTRUM	$1500–$3500	GOOD DETECTION OF MOST OPERATIONAL RADIO DEVICES
10. X-RAYS	VIEW SOLID OBJECTS FOR CONCEALED DEVICES	X-RAY PHOTOGRAPHY OR FLUOROSCOPY	$1000–$3500	CAN LOCATE CONCEALED METALLIC OBJECTS OR ELECTRICAL ALTERATIONS TO EQUIPMENT
11. RADIO JAMMING SYSTEMS	JAM RADIO DEVICE TRANSMISSIONS	GENERATE AND RADIATE HASH NOISE OVER LARGE SECTIONS OF RADIO SPECTRUM	$250–$500	LIMITED
12. AUDIO JAMMING	JAMS MICROPHONES	PRODUCES AUDIO NOISE LOCAL AREA TO MASK CONVERSATION	$50–$2500	IF USED PROPERLY WILL EFFECTIVELY DISRUPT ABILITY OF EAVESDROPPING DEVICE TO RECEIVE AUDIO SOUND
13. AUDIO PROTECTION ROOMS	ISOLATE SENSITIVE CONVERSATIONS FROM POTENTIAL EAVESDROPPING	PREVENT SOUND FROM CARRYING TO MICROPHONE THROUGH PROTECTIVE WALLS	$10,000–$30,000	VERY EFFECTIVE
14. RADIO FREQUENCY SHIELDED ROOMS	PREVENT RADIO TRANS-MISSIONS FROM LOCAL AREA	BLOCK PASSAGE OF RADIO FREQUENCY ENERGY	$25,000–$50,000	VERY EFFECTIVE
15. METAL DETECTORS	LOCATE METALLIC OBJECTS	SENSE CHANGES IN MAGNETIC FIELD CAUSED BY HIDDEN METAL OBJECT	$25–$350	CAN LOCATE METALLIC OBJECTS CONCEALED IN NON-METALLIC SURROUNDINGS

TABLE IV

3.0 Intercept of Non-Audio Information

The communication of clear audio signals suitable for interception and interpretation by the human ear is only a limited portion of the information which is freely exchanged daily. This communication process involves the transmission of information between people and machines, between two or more machines, or between imaging devices and cameras. Non-oral communications can be very attractive to the electronic surveillance specialist. This section presents a discussion of the threat of eavesdropping within these non-oral communications areas to illustrate the use and feasibility of this unique surveillance problem.

3.1 Bulk Data Communications Systems

The intercept of communications from room transmitters, body transmitters, and telephone wiretapping represents only a limited portion of the potential for intercepting of communications. Today telephone lines are frequently replaced by microwave links which stretch across nations. Many channels of communications are combined into a microwave link, and energy is beamed from tower to tower. The actual intercept of a microwave transmission may be accomplished by using a radio receiver of suitable frequency and performance capability, provided it is placed in the beam of transmitted energy. The intercept of microwave tower transmissions certainly does not provide an easily understood source of audio information because it does require extensive processing to separate communication channels which are continuously being used.

A strong candidate system for replacement of microwave communication links are millimeter wave links which operate at much higher frequencies. Instead of propagating between towers, millimeter waves are propagated via underground conduits and are much less susceptible to interception. Another technology being developed for bulk communication employs fiber optics and light energy to transmit tens of thousands of data channels simultaneously. These glass fibers provide long, wire-like light transmission paths which replace bulky copper cables. A single fiber can replace many wire channels because of greater signal carrying ability. Fiber optics communication links would be highly resistive to interception for two reasons: first, the eavesdropper would have difficulty in coupling energy from the fiber into the intercept system, and secondly, very sophisticated processing would be required to recover and separate the audio channel of interest.

Over various communication links pass a large variety of non-audio communications including teletype, data-phone, facsimile, and computer data. This non-audio information may contain company proprietary information, financial data, or personal data relative to criminal information. Intercept of this information is currently not restricted by Title III, since it cannot be classed as aural communication. Conveniently for the eavesdropper, intercept of data transmitted in much of the described media is compatible with many of the surveillance transmitters, coupling networks, and recording systems described in earlier sections of this report. Since data transmission is frequently restricted to voice grade communication channels, it is often susceptible to intercept by devices designed for audio eavesdropping. This being the case, it is conceivable that a manufacturer could openly sell a legal wiretap transmitter for use in the surreptitious interception of computer data. This survey did not include extensive investigations into the extent of data surveillance systems, but research indicates that data intercept activities, though difficult to implement, are increasing because of cost effectiveness and low risk of capture.

3.2 Computer Systems

There are over 130,000 computer systems installed in U.S. government and industrial facilities today representing a capital investment in excess of $29.2 billion.[27] These systems handle information such as credit accruals and transactions, bank and financial institution records, stock transactions, stored data bases, credit records, and proprietary industrial data. The rewards for gathering this sensitive information through computer manipulation encourages the sophisticated criminal to expend a great deal of effort to obtain it. For example, in New York City in 1974, a bank teller was able to transfer $1.5 million to his own account without leaving any trace of this activity, completely bluffing both the automated and manual accounting systems. An engineering student gained access to the computerized supply system of a telephone company and claims to have obtained and sold nearly $1 million worth of inventoried equipment before capture.

Electronic computer surveillance and manipulation can be divided into three areas: monitoring, interfering, and spoofing.[28] In the monitor activity, the legitimate user's data transferral is intercepted through a suitable wiretap or radio transmitter designed to transmit such data to a listening post to be recorded. In this activity the eavesdropper monitors the exchange of data from terminal to main computer, thereby tabulating input data and computer responses. This information in itself may be the object of the penetration activity. However, it is more likely that it is a prelude to a more sophisticated manipulation scheme requiring knowledge of the system operation, identity numbers, and the automated audit technique of the target's remote terminal.

Interfering with the normal computer function is the denial to the legitimate user of correct computer services. This includes the entering of false messages or modification of the user's message. This particular mode of surveillance activity is of particular concern to banking institutions and stock brokerage firms. This penetration can be implemented by tapping the telephone or transmission lines used between a remote terminal and a second keyboard terminal or perhaps a mini-computer that is programmed to communicate with the main computer. The cost for this activity may be $3000 to $5000, or more, for the equipment, plus the time necessary to acquire knowledge of the automated auditing and account confirmation system which always exists between the remote terminal and the central computer. After this operation is clearly defined, and the eavesdropper knows the target account numbers and verification codes, a computer is used for the manipulation operation. If the objective is only to obtain information and not to alter it, this may be the end of the process. If not, the last step is spoofing the computer into doing something erroneous.

Spoofing the computer requires extensive computer manipulation and more than interference or modification of a user's message. In this case, knowledge gained from the monitoring activity is applied to the development of a capability for the surveillance technician to enter the target's computer system by use of a remote terminal. The perpetrator identifies himself as a legitimate user, provides the legitimate identity numbers and other identifying data, and uses the computer in the same manner as a legitimate operator. In this case, depending on the degree of manipulation required, the unauthorized user can manipulate credit files, personnel records, and bank accounts with little or no danger of being apprehended.

As previously stated, many audio surveillance methods can be used for computer penetrations. By using a standard audio cassette tape recorder, the computer eavesdropper may record the necessary code data coming from a remote terminal and play it back to gain access at a later time. The terminal data input is a series of audio tones which uses the telephone lines for transmission and is therefore compatible with other audio devices including tape recorders. Computer systems which are designed to prevent access to restricted data bases by unauthorized users often inadvertently provide the eavesdropper with the additional knowledge

required. Attempts to penetrate and provide erroneous identity data prompt the computer to identify this fact and inform the user that a mistake in data entry has been attempted. In many instances shared systems control access by use of an account number, and as long as a chargeable account is provided and a customer can be billed for computer use time, the computer system is satisfied that the use is legitimate.

The best protection from penetration is provided by the main operating program within the computer system.[29] Its functions are to receive and verify access by verifying account numbers, controlling all communications with all terminals, scheduling time use, and protecting user data against inadvertent destruction. This operating program should be augmented by additional access codes for certain file data such as payrolls, or it should restrict certain users from altering data without approval. In some cases, a poorly executed penetration attempt may appear only as an "operator error". To decrease the susceptibility of the system to penetration, it is necessary to increase the effort and expense required for successful penetration. This can be achieved by improving the operating system integrity and control programs by realtime monitoring to identify unusually high levels of activity, noting excessive numbers of rejected requests for data, and requiring positive user identification through the use of additional or one-time-use pass words.

Concern for the computer security problem has become so great that the National Bureau of Standards has designed an inexpensive module to encrypt and decrypt digital data; the module can be installed on remote terminals and computer base systems to allow the legitimate user an improved level of security.[30]

3.3 Optical Processing Systems

Optical systems that are more susceptible to eavesdropping penetrations include picture telephones and private closed circuit television links. The intercept of visual data from either of these systems is feasible and, if of sufficient value to the eavesdropper, could be implemented with electronic devices available today.

4.0 Electronic Aids to Physical Surveillance

The process of physical surveillance may be aided by various electronic devices which facilitate visual monitoring at night, vehicle or cargo tracking, or precision navigation. These devices, as they apply to law enforcement and security practices, are identified and evaluated in this section of the report.

4.1 Night Viewing Systems

Before 1969 the only unclassified night viewing systems were active infrared (IR) illumination systems. Use of these devices requires that the area under surveillance be illuminated by an IR spotlight source such as an incandescent or Xenon lamp with appropriate optical filters. The filters prevent the passage of visible light but allow the passage of non-visible infrared energy. The original night viewing systems were designed to detect the reflected IR and convert it into visual light for viewing. In 1969 the first generation of visible light intensifier (amplifier) was made available to law enforcement personnel. These low light level devices require no active illumination and rely upon available ambient light from the moon, stars, or background street lighting. These night imaging devices produce an image on a small screen by amplifying the available light to a level which allows direct viewing with the naked eye. After July 1971, the second generation device was declassified by the U.S. military departments and again made available for law enforcement use. This second generation light intensifier produced a better quality picture than earlier models. These devices exist today and are used in many law enforcement applications.

4.1.1 Passive Imaging Systems. Passive imaging systems use available, ambient energy which may be either heat generated, as in the case of infrared, or energy in the visable light spectrum resulting from low level illuminations. All passive imaging systems amplify these energies to provide usable visual images to the operator, TV camera, or photographic system.

The smallest passive light intensifying system currently offered by manufacturers is approximately 8 to 12 inches in length, has a direct viewing eyepiece, and is commonly mounted on a pistol grip or camera mount.[31] Pistol grip units can resolve a man-sized target at approximately 575 feet under starlight conditions. The price of this equipment is in the $2500 to $4000 range. These small, battery-powered units are designed to operate for approximately 40 hours, are compact, light weight, and are available with various lens systems to provide various viewing ranges as well as zoom capabilities. They weigh from 3 to 4 pounds depending on lens attachments and will amplify received light 35,000 to 60,000 times.

Larger versions of these portable units are available which mount on small tripods. One overseas supplier offers a unit which weighs 37 pounds, is 30 inches in length, and 10.25 inches in diameter. Under starlight conditions, this night observation device (NOD), according to manufacturer's specifications, can detect a man-sized object at 4500 feet,

and under moonlight conditions at 6000 feet. The price of this equipment is in the $5000 to $10000 range. The image quality of the NOD is on the order of standard, commercial television. One U.S. manufacturer offers a night vision system for $4300 to $5200, depending on various, optional lens and photographic attachments. Other accessories include video and audio tape recorders, and short range radio transmitters which allow a night viewing television system to transmit its image to a remote point for viewing. These systems have numerous security applications for both law enforcement and industrial facilities. The radio transmitters used in these systems operate in the 400 to 900 MHz frequency range, have power output of 2 to 5 watts, measure 2 x 2 x 4 inches, and weigh 1.5 to 3 pounds without power supply.

Passive IR night viewing devices are less expensive and generally cost about one fifth the price of a light intensifying system. These imagers are offered in hand-held, binocular versions. They detect the infrared light energy reflected or emitted from the target and focus this energy onto a special electronic imaging tube which converts the IR into visible light. These are primarily of interest to law enforcement personnel for detection and observation of various targets. Under low light conditions, these IR systems can detect a man up to 500 feet and permit recognition at distances up to 150 feet because of their ability to detect and use sizeable amounts of IR heat energy emanting from human beings.

4.1.2 Active Imaging Systems. Active imaging systems operate by supplying non-visual IR energy to the scene under surveillance and are not dependent upon illumination from other sources. This illumination can be provided from other than the point where the viewing occurs. Incandescent lamps or 40 watt tungsten bulbs are used with an optical filter attachment to obscure the visible light. These spotlights illuminate a field of view up to 450 feet from the energy source. With the development of electronic solid state technology, these IR illumination sources have been replaced with diode or laser sources producing a much more compact illumination system. A few manufacturers offer these devices in pistol grip configurations with separate IR spotlights which, though less expensive than the passive devices, can produce equivalent results.

4.1.3 Electro-Optical Solid State Imaging. Recent developments in solid state technology have allowed development of devices which can be substituted for the standard imaging or vidicon tube used in television cameras. These solid state imaging sensors consist of an array of ten thousand or more micro-miniature light sensors assembled in a small 0.25 inch square. When combined with the necessary electronics and lens systems, a complete miniature television camera measuring only 3 x 3 x 1.88 inches and weighing only 11 ounces can be produced. However, the image quality is generally inferior to the standard television picture. These miniature cameras operate with modified commercial closed circuit television receivers and video (television picture) recorders and thus find application where conventional television is required but is too bulky and the picture quality is less important. These devices are rugged and consume little power, making them ideal for secretive viewing applications. This television camera, for example, has been offered for sale concealed in a normal home thermostat control.

One principal attraction of the solid state imaging systems, aside from the small size, is their suitability for special image processing techniques not possible with conventional systems. These techniques allow computer processing of data coming from the light sensor array and permit picture improvements by varying shades of gray, contrasts, and intensity. These miniature cameras are offered by manufacturers in this country for approximately $4,000 and will undoubtedly find wide use in future video surveillance systems. Options offered with these systems include fiber optic bundles[32] and r-f transmitters. The fiber optic bundles allow television viewing around corners and over distances where unusual physical constraints prevent easy device installation. The r-f transmitters allow remote viewing without the use of coaxial television cables.

Another electronic photographic device uses conventional film cameras integrated into packages suitable for concealment, which electronically time picture sequencing to permit area surveillance over extended periods of time. These photographic devices are offered concealed in telephones, file cabinets, office wall clocks, hi-fi speakers, attache cases, and burglar alarm control boxes. In the larger installations, a two hundred foot roll of film with pictures taken every two to three minutes, a week of physical activity in a given area can be photographically recorded if the system is activated during normal office hours. The manufacturer offers this system to aid in the discovery of vandalism and employee theft. Use of this surveillance equipment cuts labor costs of guard services for the investment of $700 to $1000 per camera system or lease of the equipment for $100 per month.

4.2 Tracking Systems

Vehicle and cargo tracking and location systems are widely used by law enforcement officers and by private industry and are becoming more useful as the systems become more able to provide better directional information. The content of this study section addresses the current technology of these tracking systems.

4.2.1 Radio Direction Finding. Radio direction finding (RDF) is the most widely used technique for providing covert tracking operations as well as agent security.[33] RDF devices operate by rotating a special antenna to establish the direction from which a received signal is strongest. This process is done automatically in most modern systems to acquire the resulting directional information. By establishing several lines of direction to a beacon transmitter from different locations, it is possible to determine the position of the beacon emitter at the point where these lines cross.

Use of all RDF systems requires the placement of a beacon transmitter, frequently called a "bumper beeper", on the target vehicle or in cargo containers. These beacon transmitters are frequently offered for sale independent of any radio direction finding receiver at prices from $100 to $500. Beacons which have their own batteries commonly have average signal outputs of 50mw to one watt and operate, depending upon the duty cycle or frequency of signal transmission, for 10 to 100 hours. These units typically measure 2 x 5 x 3 inches including battery pack. They typically transmit a radio frequency "tone burst" to be received by a radio receiver tuned to its frequency. Surface-to-surface range in an open environment for beacon systems is one to three miles; when the beacon is used in the center city environment, the range may be only a few city blocks. Surface-to-air transmission distances may be greater and ranges of 50 to 100 miles would not be uncommon if no r-f shielding inhibits the beacon transmission or the tracking aircraft's reception. Larger powered transmitters using the target automobile's twelve-volt battery system operate in essentially the same manner, but with greatly increased power output, frequently one or more watts of r-f energy, which extends effective surface range to five miles.

Bumper beeper transmitters, using the automobile battery for power, range in price from $100 to over $1000, depending on the quality of the device. Frequently the less expensive units are not very secure and can be accidently detected by the target vehicle's car radio or portable FM radio because of the many harmonics generated. As the cost and quality of the devices increase, the transmitted tone bursts vary in complexity. In some cases, multiple bursts of radio energy will be transmitted. In one system, a high energy burst transmission with a 1200 Hz tone is transmitted immediately before a low energy burst modulated with an 800 Hz tone. If the tracking receiver detected only the 1200 Hz tone, the beacon is far away. If both tones are detected, the beacon is much closer. Some beacon transmitters are integrated with remote control switch receivers for remote switching to conserve battery power and reduce the probability of detection.

Several manufacturers supply the necessary receiving equipment for use with beacon transmitters. These receivers use direction finding loop antennas or interferometer measurement techniques to determine the direction of the beacon transmitter. The indication to the operator of the receiver is not only the audible tone indicating that the beacon is in range, but also, on some equipment, a left-right needle indicator which points the way to the target and indicates its relative motion. Each of these techniques establishes direction through some form of radio signal phase measurement as the signal arrives at the receiver antenna. In the city environment, however, the performance and quality of these systems degrades substantially due to multiple signal reflections from buildings and constantly changing propagation paths between the two vehicles. This degradation is so severe in some inner-city, high-rise environs that the usefulness of the radio beacon tracking system is virtually nil. Successful use of these systems is highly dependent on operator skill and experience because of these questionable performance characteristics.

Cost of the complete system ranges from $2500 to $5000, depending on the number of channels, the receiver display, sensing electronics, and processing techniques. One manufacturer in the New England area produces a system which is a variation of the electronic tag theft control system. According to him, this tracking system is useful for area control to short ranges of two to three hundred yards. It is quite expensive, costing upwards to $10,000.

4.2.2 Time Difference of Arrival Systems. A second type of positioning system is described by the terminology—time difference of arrival system.[34] Basically, this system determines the position of a remote object that has affixed to it a special type of beacon transmitter. The pulse of energy sent by the transmitter is received at three or more widely dispersed receiving sites. Because of the finite time required for the radio pulse to travel from the target to a given receiver site, each receiver site receives the energy pulse with a slightly different time delay. The difference between the time of arrival at sites one, two, and three is measured precisely in tenths of microseconds. With this knowledge the position of the remote object can be fixed relative to the three receiving sites. Theoretically, these systems can provide precise position of numerous remote objects operating within transmitting range of the three sites. Unfortunately, these systems suffer from multi-path and propagation problems much the same as other direction finding systems. More pronounced, however, is the problem of finding a suitable frequency for operation in the congested radio spectrum.

Other time-difference-of-arrival systems designed for precision offshore seismic oil exploration operate in higher frequency bands, but they also suffer multi-path propagation problems. In these systems, the transmitters may be at fixed sites with the receiving stations on the remote object, for example, a ship. Using various timing and transponding techniques, position can be determined through measurement of arrival times between pulses. One manufacturer offering a quality vehicle location system developed this system through experience in marine direction finding.

None of these time-difference-of-arrival systems is currently in active use for vehicle location. Systems of this nature are restricted to offshore work and radar ranges.

4.2.3 Coordinate Systems. Coordinate type positioning systems are those systems wherein the target can uniquely signal its position in the form of map coordinates without the aid of a base station or other receiver-processor facility. The radio positioning system which is finding increased use in this country is called Loran, an acronym for long range radio navigation. This system has evolved over 20 years of radio positioning work and has been operational in the eastern portion of this country for several years with the western portion scheduled for coverage by the end of 1976. This radio system is a multi-user system suited principally for cooperative users and allows police, emergency vehicles and aircraft to uniquely identify position on the highway for traffic analyses, accident reporting, emergency response to civic needs, or navigation.[35] This technology is just evolving, and miniature Loran positioning sensors are now available from one manufacturer. Repeatable accuracy is frequently better than 250 feet, and costs are projected to be in the $1000 to $3000 per vehicle range when used in quantity.

A similar system, Decca, is a shorter range version of Loran and is used widely in Europe. The sensor technology for this system has not been refined sufficiently for it to be considered a viable vehicle location concept.

The Omega radio navigation system is a positioning system which should be operational within the next three to five years. At this date, however, limited coverage exists in portions of this country permitting the receipt of suitable signals from transmitters located thousands of miles away; it is reportedly able to determine the position of a target at a distance of 1 to 5 miles. The Omega systems perform well in aircraft and vessels at sea but have not proven to be suitable for vehicle location because of susceptibility to noise, vehicle motion, and expensive computer processing required for a completely automated positioning.

For several years the use of existing broadcast stations other than AM or FM bands has been proposed for vehicle location.[36] Systems using this technology have been made to work on a limited basis, though they too are range limited, and operation is restricted to areas having a sufficient number of commercial broadcast transmitters and terrain features compatible with station geometry. Positioning systems utilizing this technology may continue to evolve and may be useful for covert tracking in the future.

Another vehicle location system is one which is similar to an aircraft inertial system and requires no radio grid or other aid to determine position.[37] These systems have various sensors which detect the motion of the vehicle. Its turns, velocity, acceleration, are all processed in a computer to determine how far the vehicle has travelled and in what direction since its last known position, thereby determining its new position. This technology is still developing. At this time, it is quite expensive and its performance has not yet been proven to be as good over large areas as it has been for other vehicle tracking systems.

Most of these coordinate type systems have evolved from aerospace and aircraft technologies and are just now finding their way into the law enforcement, security, management control, and traffic analysis fields. Most are suitable for use in cooperative vehicle location and not readily adaptable to covert surveillance work.

5.0 Projection of Surveillance Technology

This section presents a view of future audio and visual surveillance technologies and projects the potential developments within these technological areas which may be expected to occur within the next ten years. None of these eavesdropping technologies or devices is expected to result from a need for better electronic surveillance equipment. Rather, they will be adjuncts to technologies developed for general communications improvements, and like all private sector products introduced to the marketplace, will evolve under constraints of market demand and economics.

5.1 Audio Systems

Audio surveillance systems of the future will see the use of improved signal processing, improved power sources, and miniaturization. Ultimately, these systems will probably be miniature "throwaway" units that will transmit at low power levels and employ sophisticated modulation techniques. The following few paragraphs describe anticipated developments which are expected to contribute to the realization of these improved audio surveillance systems.

5.1.1 Telephone Systems. Telephone communication technology is moving rapidly toward use of the video telephone and fiber optic communication links. From a surveillance standpoint, the video telephone system and accompanying fiber optic links could provide a complete video-audio surveillance system for every subscriber. Even though conventional systems will still be in widest use and susceptible to audio eavesdropping, these new systems will be less likely to be wiretapped by unauthorized eavesdroppers because of technical complexities and associated difficulties in achieving the interception of a fiber optic channel.

5.1.2 Radio Transmitters. Current technology provides radio transmitters the size of an aspirin tablet plus an equivalent sized battery that transmits audio information two to three blocks in a quiet environment. In the future these transmitters will not be reduced in size as much as they will improve in their signal processing techniques. The new integrated circuit and micro-processor computer technology will allow the small covert eavesdropping device to process audio intelligence by noise filtering and condensing the usable information before transmission to a listening post. These improvements in signal processing will allow reduction in power consumption and increased battery life. Improvements in micro-circuit fabrication techniques will eventually allow the production of very small audio surveillance transmitters.

Battery technology today can provide small nuclear cells which offer a few milliwatts of energy for a period of five or more years, and solar cells which can operate indefinitely in the presence of a suitable light source. In the future, these power sources should become more efficient, less expensive, and size reductions should make them more compatible with fabrication and miniaturization technologies.

Following these developments could be personnel tagging and surveillance devices which can be surgically implanted and used for medical purposes or consensual tracking.

Passive radio transmitter/reflector systems which require no battery or power supply may come into greater use in surveillance technology. Microwave devices which utilize a passive reflector should become more attractive, and, as operating frequencies become higher, these devices should get smaller and ultimately be only a few inches in length.

The coherent lasers used today in laboratory demonstrations should become significantly reduced in size, cost, and power consumption.

5.1.3 Microphone Systems. Microphones that are available today are quite small, and size is not a limiting factor in surveillance practices. In the future the sensitivity and frequency response of these transducers may marginally improve with little or no variation in size. What will dramatically be improved is the knowledge and use of special purpose microphone systems for noise cancelling, filtering, and directional applications. In the future these systems may be highly selective in their frequency responses and, when coupled with the microprocessor and voice print technology, these audio systems could permit virtually automatic speaker identification with reduced, a priori, speaker voice pattern knowledge. In these advanced systems, several key characteristics will be entered into the micro-processor as individual speech identifiers and the audio system may be able to select and monitor audio communications through recognition of the individual's particular speech patterns.

5.1.4 Recording Systems. Currently, cassette recorders are claimed to exist that are the size of a pocket cigarette lighter and provide up to eight hours of audio signal recording. As new recording media are developed this length of time will extend several-fold with a corresponding reduction in recorder size. A current, rapidly expanding technology for recorder application involves charge-coupled devices (CCD) or bubble memories, which are being developed in various industrial laboratories. These devices allow trillion bit digital memories in very small volumes. When the fabrication technology is better defined, these solid state memories may replace today's analog recording systems in special purpose systems.

In the event of continued growth in solid state memory technology, the signal processing and transmission technologies will expand with conjunctive rapidity due to the flexibility and speed made available through use of the solid state recording system. These devices might record optical or r-f video information over a period of time and transmit the complete data package to the listening post.

5.2 Physical Surveillance

Imaging technologies should expand over the next several years to a point where miniature battery-powered, solid state night-viewing television cameras will be able to visually monitor vast areas and relay complex signals to a remote listening post. It is anticipated that these developments will enhance the security management practices available to law enforcement and the private sector through improved sensor performance and significantly reduced system costs.

Footnotes

[1] S. W. Daskam, "Detection of Clandestine Eavesdropping Devices," page 92, International Electronic Crime Countermeasures Conference at Edinburgh, Scotland; July 1973

[2] Daskam, page 90, See Footnote 1

[3] Daskam, page 91, See Footnote 1

[4] Raymond R. Jones, "Electronic Eavesdropping Techniques and Equipment", pages 20-21, U.S. Department of Justice, Law Enforcement Assistance Administration, August 1974, LESP-RPT-0207.00

[5] D. A. Pollack, "Methods of Electronic Surveillance", pages 109-119, Charles C. Thomas, Springfield, Illinois 1973

[6] A. W. Westin, "Privacy & Freedom", New York Antheum 1967

[7] Daskam, page 92, See Footnote 1

[8] Audio Surveillance and Countermeasures", page 10, International Association of Chiefs of Police, 1973

[9] IACP, page 12, See Footnote 8

[10] "Miniature Electret Microphones", Journal of the Audio Engineering Society, Vol 18, No. 5, pages 511-517, October 1970

[11] IACP, page 12, See Footnote 8

[12] IACP, pages 18-19, See Footnote 8

[13] IACP, pages 6-9, See Footnote 8

[14] Daskam, Samuel, "Utilization of Electronic Surveillance Equipment in Crime Countermeasures Programs," 1970.

[15] Westin, See Footnote 6

[16] IACP, page 48, See Footnote 8

[17] Daskam, See Footnote 1

[18] Daskam, See Footnote 1

[19] Daskam, page 95, See Footnote 1

[20] Daskam, See Footnote 14

[21] "Bug Killer Foils Super Snooper", *Washington Post*, October 1, 1971

[22] J.D. Newman, "Metal Detectors for Police Work", International Electronic Crime Conference, July 1973, pages 50-60

[23] IACP, See Footnote 8

[24] Westin, See Footnote 6

[25] Westin, page 83, See Footnote 6

[26] H.M. Gelfand, "Debugging Experts, Aided by Watergate, Detect Rise in Sales", *Wall Street Journal*, May 16, 1973

[27] D. Branstad; "Executive Guide to Computer Security", National Bureau of Standards, 1974

[28] D. Branstad, See Footnote 27

[29] R. Taru, and H.E. Peterson, "Security of Computerized Information Systems", Carnahan Crime Conference, April 1970, page 82

[30] D. Branstad, "Encryption Algorithim for Protecting Computer Data", National Bureau of Standards, 1975; Westin, see Footnote 6; R.J. Wilk, "Engineering Considerations in Computer Center Security," International Electronic Crime Conference, July 1973, page 244

[31] B.D. Aaron, "Surveillance Under Low Light Level Conditions", Carnahan Crime Conference, April 1971, pages 17-37

[32] Westin, See Footnote 6

[33] R.P.K. Walla, and S.G. Bacon, "Development of a Police Helicopter DF-Homing System", Carnahan Crime Conference, 1971, pages 125-147

[34] R.L. Saslaw, "An Active TDOA Locate and Trace System", Carnahan Crime Conference, April 1973, page 157

[35] W.K. Vogler, "Vehicle Location with Loran C", Carnahan Crime Conference, May 19, 1975, page 173-180

[36] G.D. Wilson, "Cargo Security System", Carnahan Crime Conference May 1975, pages 126-134

[37] Wilson, See Footnote 36

GLOSSARY

ACTIVE IMAGING Forming a visual image on a screen of a low light scene by using an IR illumination source. Not dependent on available light energy to electronically form picture.

AMPLIFIER Electrical circuit that makes a small signal larger by increasing its voltage or power level.

ANTENNA A length of wire that gathers radio signals for a receiver or emits them from a transmitter.

AGENT TRANSMITTER Small radio transmitter concealed on a person's body used for agent or informer protection or consensual monitoring.

ANTIBUG Radio noise generator designed to interfere with bugs.

ATTENUATION A reduction in strength or energy of an electrical signal.

AUDIO Sound waves audible to the human ear.

AUDIO ACTUATOR (Voice actuated switch) A sound-actuated device used to turn on and off tape recorders or radio transmitters (to conserve tape or transmitter battery power).

AUDIO MONITORING Electronic device or devices designed and used to listen to conversations, sometimes from a remote point.

BANDWIDTH The extent or deviation of frequencies about a given center frequency. Also, characteristic of a radio receiver which allows information of a certain frequency and bandwidth to be received.

BODY TRANSMITTER See AGENT TRANSMITTER.

BUG Clandestine listening device; generally a small, hidden microphone and radio transmitter.

BUG DETECTOR Electronic audio surveillance countermeasures device used to locate radio bugs.

BUGGING Process of monitoring conversations by electronic means.

BUMPER BEEPER Radio beacon transmitter hidden in or on a vehicle for use with radio direction finding equipment.

CAPACITIVE PICKUP A transducer that functions by capacitance, rather than by direct connection to a circuit.

CAPACITOR (CONDENSER) Circuit component that stores electrical energy. Two metal plates separated by insulation which block d.c. but pass a.c. signals.

CARBON MICROPHONE A microphone that depends for its operation upon the variation in resistance of carbon granules.

CARRIER Radio-frequency signal of constant amplitude upon which information may be added by means of modulation.

CATHODE RAY TUBE Television like display tube.

CAVITY RESONATOR Type of microwave transducer that modulates a microwave beam in the presence of audio frequencies.

CHEESE BOX An electronic device connected between two telephone lines, used to prevent call tracing, which will, with the caller's knowledge, enable his call to be completed to another telephone.

CLOSED CIRCUIT TELEVISION Television signals transmitted by coaxial cable or microwave systems.

COHERENT Electro-magnetic energy where all individual waves of one frequency are locked in phase in orderly fashion compared to non-coherent waves which are random.

COIL Inductor-Circuit component that stores electrical energy as a magnetic field. A winding of wire used to sense magnetic field fluctuations.

CONSENSUAL MONITORING Description of legal situation wherein conversation between two individuals is monitored with the knowledge of one of the participants.

CONTACT MICROPHONE (Spike Microphone) A specially constructed microphone designed to be attached directly to the surface to be monitored. This type of microphone generally responds only when the object or surface is vibrated.

COUNTERMEASURES Defensive techniques designed to detect, prevent, or expose the use of electronic audio or visual surveillance devices.

CONNECTOR BLOCK See TERMINAL BLOCK

CRYSTAL MICROPHONE A microphone that depends for its operation on the generation of an electric charge by the deformation of a crystal.

DATA LINK Point-to-point radio communication channel designed primarily for transmission of data rather than audio signals.

DEBUGGING Process of conducting electronic audio surveillance countermeasures operations. Countermeasures.

DEMODULATION Process of retrieving audio information from a modulated r-f signal.

DIAL MECHANISM Numbered rotating wheel on telephone instrument to generate calling impulses of numbered dialed. Newer telephones use touch tones for same purpose.

DIRECTIONAL MICROPHONE A microphone that is extremely sensitive to audio frequencies arriving from one particular direction, while rejecting those that arrive from other directions.

DROP-IN MOUTHPIECE A telephone radio tap transmitter concealed in a case that has the appearance of a telephone carbon mouthpiece.

EAVESDROPPING Secretly listening or recording of conversations; includes both bugging and wire-tapping.

ELECTRONIC STETHOSCOPE Contact microphone or physician's stethoscope equipped with an electronic amplifier.

FEDERAL OR GOVERNMENT SECTOR Governmental agencies, may include law enforcement, or investigative organizations.

FEEDBACK Regeneration of a signal. One method used for detection of radio transmitter bugs.

FIELD STRENGTH METER An electronic radio field detection device that detects the presence of r-f energy. Field detector.

FILTER Electrical circuit that accepts (or rejects) a particular band of frequencies.

FREQUENCY MODULATION (FM) Method of modulation by which intelligence is impressed on a carrier by varying the frequency of the carrier.

GOVERNMENT SECTOR See FEDERAL SECTOR

GROUND WIRE Conductor leading from a device to an earth ground connection.

HANDSET The part of the telephone instrument used for talking and listening.

HARMONICS Frequencies of exact multiple of a fundamental or carrier frequency.

HARDWIRE Use of wire pair rather than radio transmitter to communicate information between two points.

HARMONICA BUG See INFINITY BUG.

HASH Electrical noise.

HERTZ (Hz) International unit of frequency equal to one cycle per second. Kilohertz (KHz1,000 Hz), Megahertz (MHz-1,000,000 Hz), Gigahertz (GHz1,000,000,000 Hz).

HOOK SWITCH Switch in telephone instrument actuated by the plunger on which the handset rests when not in use.

HOT MIKE Activation of the microphone of a telephone in the "hung-up" position through the use of a third wire tap, silicon controlled rectifier, or other electronic components. Also see THIRD-WIRE TAP.

IMPEDANCE Resistance to the flow of alternating current. The combined effect of resistance, inductance and capacitance.

IMPEDANCE MATCHING The circuit arrangement required to adjust the impedance of an alternating current circuit to the value recommended for proper operation.

INDUCTION TAP Wiretap that makes use of a coil placed around or near the telephone line or instrument. Operates on the principle of electromagnetic induction.

INDUCTIVE PICKUP A magnetic transducer that functions by the principle of electro magnetic-induction, rather than by direct connection to a circuit.

INFINITY BUG An audio amplifier and microphone connected to a telephone line through an audio-tone sensitive relay which is activated by telephoning the bugged premises and sounding the coded tone.

INFINITY TRANSMITTER See INFINITY BUG

INFRARED (IR) Light waves too low in frequency to be seen by the human eye; produced by thermal radiation.

INFRARED VIEWER Device that makes infrared light visible to the human eye.

JAMMER An r-f or audio frequency generating oscillator that interferes with the operation of an electronic audio surveillance system.

JAMMING The intentional transmission of interfering signals in order to disturb the reception of other signals.

LASER Device used to generate an intense monochromatic (single color) frequency or light beam.

LASER PICK-OFF Electronic audio surveillance through the use of coherent light waves reflected from a surface vibrating at an audio frequency rate.

LEASED LINE Dedicated telephone line leased to customer for specific communications use.

LINE AMPLIFIER An audio amplifier used to provide preamplification of an audio signal before transmitting the signal over a transmission line. Use of a line amplifier permits extending the audio transmission distance between two points when used with a low impedance line driver.

LINE MATCHING NETWORK Circuit that provides for optimal transfer of audio signal from phone line to wiretap equipment.

LISTENING POST Location where eavesdropper monitors receiving equipment during bugging operations.

MAGNETIC TAPE RECORDER Device that records sound on magnetic tape.

MICROWAVES Radio frequencies generally higher than 1,000 MHz.

MODULATOR Electronic circuitry used to impress information on a carrier by instantaneously varying its amplitude (AM) or frequency (FM).

MONITORING The act of listening-in or eavesdropping on telephone lines or room conversations.

MOVING COIL MICROPHONE A moving conductor microphone in which the moveable conductor is in the form of a coil where an electric output results from the motion of the coil in a magnetic field at an audio frequency rate.

MULTIPATH The possible multiple routes for a single beam of r-f energy between two points caused by many reflecting surfaces.

NARROW BAND FM Special form of FM modulation where the deviation caused by the modulation process about the main carrier is less than normal..

OPTICAL FIBERS Glass fibers used to transmit light energy.

OSCILLATOR Electrical circuit that produces an audio tone or a radio frequency carrier.

PANORAMIC DISPLAY A device designed to display all signals present in a given frequency band as vertical pulses on a horizontal trace.

PARABOLIC MICROPHONE Microphone with a large disk-like attachment used for listening to audio from great distances.

PARALLEL RADIO TAP Radio tap transmitter which is attached across both wires of a phone line.

PASSIVE IMAGING Forming a visual picture or image on a screen of a low light content scene without the aid of illumination.

PASSIVE REFLECTOR Resonant cavity. Metallic cylinder which reflects r-f energy at a particular frequency.

PEN REGISTER Instrument that records telephone dial pulses as inked dashes on paper tape. Dial impulse recorder. A touch-tone decoder performs the same function for a touch-tone telephone.

PERSISTANCE DISPLAY Cathode ray tube which retains or stores an image visually once the electrical input signal is gone.

PHASE MEASUREMENT Measuring a fraction of a single cycle.

POWER SUPPLY Device that supplies power to electronic equipment.

PRIVATE SECTOR Non-government community; includes individuals or private industry.

PROPAGATION Travel of an electro-magnetic radio wave through space.

QUICK PLANT Audio bugging transmitter easily installed or dropped in target area.

RADIO FREQUENCY (RF) Electro-magnetic waves used in radio communications to carry information.

RDF Radio-direction-finding.

RECEIVER Earphone in telephone handset, or, radio signal reception and demodulation device.

REGENERATIVE FEEDBACK Squeal caused by the output of an amplifier feeding back to its own input. FEEDBACK.

RELAY Electrically operated switch. May be a current-actuated relay, voltage-drop relay, tuned relay, or voice relay.

RESISTOR Circuit component that resists the flow of current.

RESONANCE The condition whereby an electrical circuit responds with maximum effect or amplitude to an applied frequency causing a maximum flow of current or high voltage level.

RESONANT CAVITY Hollow metal cylinder whose dimensions are chosen to make it strongly reflect a radio signal of predetermined frequency. Passive Reflector.

RINGER Telephone bell and the electrical circuit that makes it work.

SCRAMBLER Commonly, a speech-inversion and/or frequency-inversion device that codes audio frequencies so that they are not comprehensible to the unaided ear. May also be sophisticated digital device which changes voice into a digital form at the transmission end and/or reconverts it to understandable voice at the receiving end.

SCREAMER An r-f field strength and audio amplifier combination that causes feedback when positioned near a concealed transmitter. Also known as a "howler" or "squealer".

SERIES RADIO TAP Radio transmitter which usually obtains power from the telephone line to which it is attached and is installed in series or in line with one wire.

SHOTGUN MIKE Highly directional microphone with tube-like appearance.

SIDE BAND The small band of frequencies produced adjacent to a main radio carrier frequency which contains the basic audio information.

SILENT ROOMS Areas shielded acoustically against eavesdropping. Also known as Acoustic Rooms.

SPIKE MIKE Contact type microphone with a long, needle-like extension used for listening through walls.

STANDING WAVES A pattern of radio energy in space which varies in intensity from point to point caused by reflections of radio signals.

SURVEILLANCE Secretly observing the behavior of another, includes both audio eavesdropping and visual monitoring.

SURVEILLANCE RECEIVER Radio receiver used to monitor radio transmitter bugs or beacons.

TECHNICAL SURVEILLANCE Bugging, wire-tapping, televising or radio tracking techniques.

TELEPHONE INSTRUMENT The complete telephone set, including handset, ringer and all other associated parts.

TERMINAL BLOCK Point at which individual telephone instruments are connected to the interior phone lines of a building.

TERMINAL BOX Point at which telephone lines are spliced or connected to cables.

THIRD WIRE TAP The activating of a telephone microphone by adding a third wire to the circuit, so that the telephone microphone may be activated while the handset is "hung-up" bypassing the hook switch.

TOUCH TONE DIAL Push-button telephone dial.

TRANSDUCER A device which converts one form of energy to another, e.g., sound to electrical.

TRIANGULATION Process used to locate a beacon by use of multiple direction-finding receivers (see RDF).

TRIGGER TRANSMITTER Device used to turn on a remotely located bug on command through switch receiver.

ULTRAHIGH FREQUENCIES (UHF) Radio frequencies in the approximate range from 300 MHz to 3,000 MHz.

ULTRASONIC Sound waves too high in frequency to be heard by the human ear; generally above 20 KHz.

ULTRAVIOLET (UV) Light wave too high in frequency to be seen by the human eye.

VERY HIGH FREQUENCY (VHF) Radio frequencies in the approximate range from 30 MHz to 300 MHz.

VOICE ACTUATED SWITCH (Audio Actuator) (VOX) - Switch that closes when conversation is impressed at its input. Used to turn on and off electronic devices.

VOLT METER Electronic device used to measure voltage levels.

WALL CONNECTOR BLOCK See TERMINAL BLOCK

WIRELESS MICROPHONE Very low power short range radio transmitter legitimately used by entertainers and sports casters as microphones. Used by eavesdroppers as inexpensive listening devices.

WIRETAP Clandestine interception of a telephone conversation away from the target premises.

GENERAL BIBLIOGRAPHY

Aaron, Betram D., "Surveillance Under Low Light Level Conditions", Carnahan Crime Conference, April 22-24, 1971

Adrian, D.J., Christensen, L.E., and Smith, R.D., "Automatic Vehicle Location Systems Using A Low Frequency Hyperbolic Reference Guide", Carnahan Crime Conference, April 22-24, 1971

Anders, R.A., Menal, W.G., and McCoy, E.E., "Miniature T.V. Camera Utilizing Photo Transistor Sensor Arrays", Carnahan Crime Conference, April 22-24, 1971

Beek, Bruno, and Grech, James, "Experimental Techniques for Automatic Speaker Identification", Carnahan Crime Conference, April 22-24, 1971

Beukers, J.E., and Meranda, J.I., "The Practical Application of Loran C Radio Signals to the Precision Location and Tracking of Remote Objects", Carnahan Crime Conference, April 22-24, 1971

Bolt, Bernaek, and Newman, Inc., "A Survey of the Present and Probable Future State of Technology Affecting Privacy Report No. 1008", prepared for the Special Committee on Science and Law, Carnahan Crime Conference, April 22-24, 1971

Branstad, D., "Encryption Algorithim for Protecting Computer Data", National Bureau of Standards

Branstad, D., "Executive Guide to Computer Security", National Bureau of Standards

Brown, Robert M., "The Electronic Invasion", 1967, John F. Ryder, New York

Butterwick, G.N., and Stoudenheimer, R.G., "Second Generation Image Intensifiers in Law Enforcement Applications", Carnahan Crime Conference, April 19-21, 1972

Carroll, J.M., "Secrets of Electronic Espionage", 1966, Dutton, New York

Carroll, J.M., "The Third Listener", 1969, Dutton, New York

Charter, S.T., Tristan, J. David, "High Security Methods of Reporting Information", Proceedings, International Electronic Crime Countermeasures Conference, July 1973

Cramer, J.H., Streck, D., "Protection of Sensitive Information in a Law Enforcement Computer Network", Carnahan Crime Conference, April 1973

Cunningham, J.E., "Security Electronics", April 1970, Howard W. Sams & Company, Indianapolis

Dash, S., Schwartz, R.F., Knowlton, R.D., "The Eavesdroppers", Rutgers University Press, 1959

Daskam, Samuel W., "Utilization of Electronic Surveillance Equipment in Crime Countermeasures Program", Carnahan Crime Conference, April 16-18, 1970

Daskam, Samuel W., "Detection of Clandestine Eavesdropping Devices", Proceedings International Electronic Crime Countermeasures Conference, July 1973

Daskam, Samuel W., "Survey of Commonly Available Eavesdropping Devices", 1971, Mason Engineering Company

Elsalsser, G., "Systems Considerations in Implementing Low Light Level Television Cameras", Carnahan Crime Conference, April 19-21, 1972

Farrell, R.J., "Exterminating the Electronic Bugs", New York Herald Tribune, March 29, 1964

Fraim, F, & Murphy, P., "Miniature Electret Microphones", Journal of the Audio Engineering Society, Volume 18, No. 5, October, 1970

Gaskin, C.E., "Comments on Surveillance Techniques and Equipment", April 1975

Gelfand, Howard, "Debugging Experts", Wall Street Journal, May 16, 1973

Godbout, William, "Computer Theft by Computer", Security World, May 1971

Greene, Richard M., Jr., Editor, "Business Intelligence and Espionage", LC No. 66-25591, October 1966, Dow Jones-Irwin, Inc., Homewood, Illinois

Hamilton, Peter, "Computer Security", 197, London Press

Hamilton, Peter B., "Security Accuracy and Privacy in Computer Systems", 1967, Hutchinson Publishing Group, Ltd., London, England

Heckel, Donald T., "Low-Level Light TV Surveillance System", Carnahan Crime Conference, April 16-18, 1970

Herscher, M.B., Martinand, T.B., Meeker, W.F., "Automatic Speaker Identification and Verification", Carnahan Crime Conference, April 16-18, 1970

Huber, James L., "100/1000 MHz Surveillance Transmitter", Carnahan Crime Conference, April 16-18, 1970

Jackson, John, Cooper, Paul, Young, Anderson, "An Electronic Tag for Theft Control", Carnahan Crime Conference, April 19-20, 1968

Jackson, Melvin, "Night Scope for Low Light Level Surveillance", Carnahan Crime Conference, April 22-24, 1971

Jesch, L, Berry, I.S., "Batteries Used with Law Enforcement Communications Equipment, Comparison and Performance Characteristics", LESP-RPT-0201.00, U.S. Department of Justice, Law Enforcement and Criminal Justice

Jones, Raymond R., "Electronic Eavesdropping Techniques and Equipment", LESP RPT 0207.00. August 1974, U.S. Department of Justice LEAA. National Institute of Law Enforcement and Criminal Justice

Kaplan, G.S., Staras, H., "An X-Band Sign Post Vehicle Location System", Carnahan Crime Conference, April 19-21, 1972

Kersta, L.G., "Voice Pattern Identification of Speakers", Carnahan Crime Conference, April 19-20, 1968

Kesler, Ronald, "New Bug-Killer Developed to Foil Secret Telephonic Super Snooper", *Washington Post,* October 1, 1971

Kwitney, Jonathan, "Listening In", *Wall Street Journal,* October 5, 1973

Luck, James E., "Descrption of a Real Time Completely Automatic Speaker Verification System", Carnahan Crime Conference, April 19-20, 1968

Martin, James, "Security Accuracy and Privacy in Computer Systems", 1974, Prentice Hall

Martinez, Al, "Industrial Spying", *Los Angeles Times,* August 19, 1974

Mason, John F., "Designers Compete for that Automatic Bug in a Rug", EDN, Volume 21, No. 20, September 27, 1973

McLean, Raymond L., Fleming, Robert B., "LOCATES Automatic Vehicle Location and Status Report System", Carnahan Crime Conference, 1973

Mills, Donia, "Big Brother is Bugging You", *Washington Star News,* April 22, 1974

Montgomery, Jim, "Concern Eavesdrops on Employees' Phone Calls", *Wall Street Journal,* March 21, 1974

Newman, J.D., "Metal Detectors for Police Use", Proceedings Internationl Electronic Crime Countermeasures Conference, July 1973

Oliver, Eric, "Practical Security in Commerce and Industry", 1972, Halsted Press

Osborne, William P., "Mixed Base Modulation - A New Technique", Carnahan Crime Conference, April 22-24 1971

Pfisher, Robert F., "Law Enforcement Applications of Surveillance Receivers", Carnahan Crime Conference, 1973

Pollock, David A., "Methods of Electronic Audio Surveillance", 1973, Charles C. Thomas, Springfield, Illinois

Renninger, C., Brandstad, "Privacy and Security in Computer Systems", Publication 809, February 1974, National Bureau of Standards

Renninger, C., "Privacy and Security in Computer Systems", Publication 404, September 1974, National Bureau of Standards

Richmond, Joseph C., Walters, Edward T., "Development of a Standard for Passive Night Vision Devices, A Progress Report"

Saslaw, Richard, L., "An Active TDOA Locate and Trace System", Carnahan Crime Conference, 1973

Shannon, C.E., "Communications Theory of Secrecy Systems", *Bell Systems Technical Journal,* Volume 28, pp 656-715, October 1969

Shaw, W., "An Introduction to Law Enforcement Electronics and Communications, Part III TV Surveillance", *Law & Order,* May 1965

Shelton, Art L., "Sensors for Surveillance Systems", Carnahan Crime Conference, April 16-18, 1970

Speer, Edward D., "LODIF - An IR Surveillance Camera", Carnahan Crime Conference, April 16-18, 1970

Stoudenheimer, R.B., Faulkner, R.D., "Night Surveillance Systems for Law Enforcement", Carnahan Crime Conference, April 16-18, 1970

Sugar, George R., "Voice Privacy Equipment for Law Enforcement Communications Systems", National Bureau of Standards, September 1973

Taru, Rein, and Peterson, Harold E., "Security of Computerized Information Systems", Carnahan Crime Conference, April 16-18, 1970

Taylor, Louis L., "Vehicle Location Systems Dependent Upon Standards Broadcast Transmissions", Carnahan Crime Conference, April 16-18, 1970

Timothy, L.K., Ball, J.F., "A Secure Voice Commo System with a Low Bit Rate and High Voice Quality", Carnahan Crime Conference, 1973

Totenberg, Nina, "Bug-Out", *National Observer,* April 8, 1972

Vogler, W.K., "Vehicle Location with Loran C," Carnahan Crime Conference, May 19, 1975.

Walla, P.K., Bacon, Stephen, G., "Development of a Police Helicopter DF-Homing System", Carnahan Crime Conference, April 16-18, 1970

Walsh, Timothy J., Healey, Richard J., "Protecting Your Business Against Espionage", 1975, Acacom Press

Walter, K.G., "Primitive Models for Computer Security", 1974, Case Western Reserve University, Cleveland, Ohio

Westin, A.W., "Privacy and Freedom", New York, 1967, Atheneum

Wilent, C.E., "Automatic Vehicle Surveillance Systems", Carnahan Crime Conference, April 19-21, 1972

Wilk, Robert J., "Enginnering Considerations in Computer Security", Proceedings International Electronic Crime Countermeasures Conference, 1973

Wilson, G.D., "Cargo Security System," Carnahan Crime Conference, May 1975

Winters, Dale, "Photo Surveillance", Carnahan Crime Conference, April 19 - 20, 1968

Young, P.A., "Thermal Viewers for Police Use", Proceedings International Electronic Crime Countermeasures Conference, July 1973

Reports & Periodicals

"Audio Surveillance and Countermeasures", Published by International Association of Chiefs of Police, 1973

Congressional Record, S648, January 23, 1975

"Electronic Eavesdropping Techniques and Equipment", Electromagnetics Division, National Bureau of Standards, August 1974

"Eavesdropping Legislation - Down-But Not Out", (Page 45) June 23, 1967 *Time*

"Electronic Investigations and Secure Communications Course, Police Electronics Institute", (Report), 1972, Chicago, Illinois

"How to Avoid Electronic Eavesdropping and Privacy Invasion" by the Investigators Information Service, 1967, Los Angeles, California

"Miniature Electret Microphones", *Journal of the Audio Engineering Society,* Vol. 18, No. 5, October 1970

Pinkerton Advertisement, September 5, 1974, *Wall Street Journal*

"Security Attitudes and Techniques for Management", published by Hutchinson of London, Chapter X, 1968

"Spy Supplies are the Real Adult Toys", 21 June 1973, *New Scientist*

"Surveillance by Microwave Beams", pages 89-91, *Electronics Illustrated*, January 1962

"Taps to Steal Computer Data, How Feasible?", *Security World*, May 1971

THE AUTHENTICATION OF MAGNETIC TAPES: CURRENT PROBLEMS AND POSSIBLE SOLUTIONS

Prepared by Mark R. Weiss, Queens College,
City University of New York, and Michael H. L.
Hecker, Stanford Research Institute.

FOREWORD

This report is a survey of the art of examining and authenticating magnetic tapes for legal purposes. A tape is said to be authenticated if the forensic examiner finds no evidence that the tape has been tampered with. The specific topics to be covered in this report include the requirements for introducing tapes into evidence, signs suggestive of tampering and innocuous souces of such signs, techniques that can be used to falsify tapes, and methods for detecting tape falsifications. The report concludes with a summary of the problems of authenticating tapes and some possible short-term and long-term solutions to them.

The authors of the report are particularly knowledgeable in this area. Both of them participated in the examination of the Watergate tapes and subsequently have examined numerous other tapes. Much of the material herein is drawn from their experiences. Both authors are electronics engineers with strong backgrounds in the theory and art of tape recording, the analysis and perception of speech, and the uses of sophisticated methods and instruments for the analysis of acoustic and electrical signals. Both have had many years of experience in formulating, conducting, and directing scientific investigations.

Wherever possible, the authors have tried to avoid using technical terms in the descriptions that are given for methods of falsifying and authenticating tapes. Where such terms are used they are defined. For the convenience of the reader, a glossary of all such terms, together with their definitions, is given in an appendix.

A final word of caution to the reader: this report is not a comprehensive review of techniques for detecting tape falsifications. Nor could it be. This relatively new art is still evolving; frequently, new techniques must be developed for each new tape to be examined. While the report does review the current state of this art, its power, and its limitations, the report is neither a handbook, nor a text suitable for the training of persons interested in becoming forensic examiners of tapes.

CHAPTER 1—TAPE RECORDINGS AS EVIDENCE IN COURT PROCEEDINGS

A. INTRODUCTION

This report concerns the process of authenticating tapes that may be offered into evidence in court proceedings. The terms authentic, authenticating, tape, and recording appear frequently throughout the report. While their meanings may seem obvious, it is desirable for the sake of clarity and to avoid ambiguity that the sense in which they are used be defined here.

A tape is authentic if it was, in fact, make in the manner claimed by the parties profering it as evidence. A tape is said to have been authenticated if a thorough forensic examination does not yield evidence contradicting that claim.

The term tape has two related meanings, a general one and a specific one. In its general usage, tape refers to a reel of magnetic tape upon which sounds have been recorded. The specific meaning of tape is the physical magnetic ribbon itself, exclusive of any information recorded on it. By contrast, the term recording refers to the information recorded on a tape, exclusive of the physical magnetic material.

B. REQUIREMENTS FOR ADMISSIBILITY OF TAPES INTO EVIDENCE

A witness who has lawfully heard a conversation can testify about it in court if the conversation is relevant to the issue at trial. But a recording of that conversation potentially provides the ultimate in corroboration of that witness' testimony. Indeed, the recording may have accurately caught some words, some inflections of voice, which the witness' testimony is unable to reflect. But a witness who overheard the conversations can be cross-examined on their context, whereas a recording cannot. The introduction of a tape into evidence can be most unfair if its authenticity is questionable.

When a prosecuter seeks to offer tapes into evidence, he must be ready to overcome three basic hurdles that will affect their admissibility: speech on the tapes may be partially inaudible or unintelligible, the voices of the relevant persons overheard may not be identifiable, and the defendant may claim that the tapes could have been tampered with.

1. Audibility and Intelligibility of Speech

Speech on tapes is audible to the degree to which it can be distinguished from background sounds. It is intelligible to the degree to which words that are heard can be recognized unambiguously.

Inaudibility or unintelligibility of speech on tapes is a frequently encountered problem. While lack of audibility on tapes of telephone wiretap interceptions is unusual, both inaudibility and unintelligibility occur frequently in interceptions by room microphones or body recorders. Audibility and intelligibility problems can result because of equipment failure, because there are intervening sounds (background noise) obscuring the recorded voice, or because the recorded conversations occurred beyond the effective range of the transmitting and intercepting devices. Once these problems occur, there is little that a prosecutor can do. To the extent that some conversations are audible and intelligible, transcripts can be prepared to aid a jury in listening to them. The recording might be played at greater volume, played on a better quality amplifier with better speakers, played into earphones, or played several times, so that a jury, with the aid of transcripts, can follow the evidence. Audio experts, using highly sophisticated and expensive equipment, can sometimes filter out background noise and thus improve the audibility of the recorded conversation. Although this process does not involve alteration of the tape, use of a "cleaned up" copy in evidence creates special problems of admissibility for the prosecutor. Audible and intelligible portions of tapes are admissible into evidence, even when part of the recording is unintelligible. The jury's determination of the facts, however, must be based on the recorded conversations and not on a transcriber's subsequent interpretation of what was said, whether or not he received the assistance of an audio expert. A juror might rely too much on the transcript, or might place too much emphasis on the playing or replaying of tapes. And there might be some danger that a conversation, surrounded by unintelligible statements, can be taken out of context. Consequently, judges may rule out all or most of a recording where a substantial part of it is unintelligible or inaudible.

2. Identifiability of Voices

A voice heard on a tape can be identified as that of a particular person only on the strength of testimony of witnesses and to the extent to which it sounds like the recorded voice of that person and unlike the recorded voices of others*. Identification can be established by the testimony of persons who have had but minimal exposure to a defendant's voice. The arresting police officer, for example, can testify on this issue. A witness' ability to identify the voice of the defendant is a matter for the jury to consider. Identification can be bolstered by voice exemplars played to the jury. It can be shown by extrinsic evidence; for example, recorded references by name to the person talking, testimony that the party was known to be in the room at the time the conversation was recorded, or testimony that the party responded to the recorded conversation by going to a meeting place or promptly doing some other act that had been discussed. Thus, there exist ample evidentiary means of linking the evidence contained in a recorded conversation to the party on trial. However, identification of the voice, together with all other proof offered to

establish a defendant's guilt, remains a jury question.

3. Authenticity of Tapes

The possibility that tapes may have been tampered with raises the most significant legal problems concerning their admissibility into evidence. Though the issue is raised infrequently, a claim of tampering constitutes the most serious challenge to the value of electronic surveillance as a means of obtaining evidence. It is not possible for a layman, judge, or juror to examine the tape itself to see if it was altered, nor can there be a direct proof in law that a tape is authentic. This is, therefore, an area where the law requires the exercise of a great degree of caution.

There are two general approaches for establishing the authenticity of a tape. Current legal practice is to place the burden of proof on the attorney seeking to introduce the tape into evidence (usually the prosecutor). As will be described below, the attorney must demonstrate that certain accepted procedures designed to protect the tape from possible tampering have been followed. The second approach, which must be resorted to if the first one fails, is to submit the tape to a qualified expert for a forensic examination. On the basis of scientific tests, the forensic examiner may be able to rule out tampering and thus demonstrate the authenticity of the tape.

When a prosecutor seeks to introduce tapes into evidence at trial, he must be prepared to show that the equipment used to make the tapes was in good working order, that it had been maintained in conformity with trade standards, and that it was installed and operated by persons experienced in the use of the equipment. They must have used brand new tapes if the recordings are to achieve the highest level of acceptability.

Because tapes can be altered, standards of admissibility into evidence have been stringent. It is an established rule of law that when an item is capable of being replaced or altered, admissibility requires that all those who have handled the item identify it and testify to its custody and unchanged condition. Thus, when investigators set out to intercept and record conversations, they will usually follow a set procedure. They will serially number the tapes, keep careful logs which note the time of particular conversations and the places on the tapes where they appear, store the tapes in separate envelopes,

_____

*In recent years, a method for identifying a person by comparing spectrograms of his voice with those of known individuals has been accepted in some courts but rejected in others. This method may have some merits for investigative purposes, but, in the opinion of most experts in speech research, it has not yet been shown to be sufficiently valid for use as evidence in judicial proceedings.

and keep written records of the custodians of these envelopes. That no unauthorized person touched the tapes may be established by use of adhesive markings or other sealing devices.

As soon as is practicable after completion of a court-ordered interception and recording, tapes are submitted to the court for the purpose of formally sealing them. Sometimes the police officer seals the tapes at the court's direction, although it is better practice for the judge to do the sealing himself. Custody of the sealed tapes is often placed with the police or prosecutor, at the court's direction.

Upon offering the tapes into evidence, the prosecutor must be prepared to establish the chain of custody of the tapes from the time they were made until the time they are proffered. Each person in this chain must be able to testify that the tapes were not tampered with while in his possession and that they were kept in such a manner that no one else could have tampered with them.

Demonstration of a chain of custody and of proper sealing of tapes is enough to indicate *prima facie* authenticity. However, such legal procedures do not guarantee that a tape has not been tampered with. Despite the most scrupulous adherence to the procedures required by law, any investigative process whereby surreptitiously intercepted conversations are recorded may be open to a claim that somewhere in the process the tapes were falsified. Tapes can be altered and re-recorded, and logs reflecting conversations that took place can be changed. Even when the proffered evidence is under judicial seal, the claim may be made that it was tampered with prior to sealing. If a party has any substantial backing for a claim that the tapes were tampered with, such as a weak link in the chain of custody or a sign suggestive of falsification, the prosecutor may be required to go further than merely establishing the safekeeping procedures. He bears the burden of proving the substantive authenticity of the tapes.

The authenticity of a tape is likely to be questioned if it exhibits unusual or not readily explainable characteristics. A prolonged loud noise, a gap in the conversation, or a sudden loss in the strength of the speech sounds can be read as a sign suggesting that the tape may have been altered. Much of the time, such signs arise from innocuous causes, as will be described in Chapter 2. The rest of the time they are the result of an attempt to falsify the tape, using procedures to be discussed in Chapter 3.

C. THE FORENSIC EXAMINATION OF TAPES

When legal procedures are not adequate to establish the authenticity of a tape, the claim that it may have been tampered with can be resolved only upon expert technical examination of the tape. The methods used in the examination must be based on a scientific approach to detecting falsifications; such an approach is described in Chapter 4. It represents the current state of this new and still evolving art.

The practical application of the approach to be described in Chapter 4 is limited by several major problems. First and most immediate is the disparity between the increasing number of tapes requiring expert examination and the very small number of qualified forensic examiners. Starting with the Watergate tape investigation, the number of requests for examination of tapes has increased steadily. Both authors are currently contacted at a rate of about once a week to assist in both civil and criminal cases but, for a lack of time, they can participate in only about one out of every six cases. On occasion, legal proceedings have had to be delayed to permit time for an examination to be made or completed. Colleagues of ours have reported similar experiences.

Since there are, as yet, no standards for qualifications of forensic examiners, attorneys who are unable to engage the services of recognized experts may well rely on inadequately qualified or even grossly unqualified personnel. The result would be to risk erroneous conclusions regarding the authenticity of tapes and their admissibility into evidence.

CHAPTER 2—SIGNS SUGGESTIVE OF FALSIFICATION AND SOME INNOCUOUS MECHANISMS BY WHICH THEY CAN OCCUR

A. INTRODUCTION

When a tape that is to be used as evidence in a court proceeding is played back, at least one of the interested parties is likely to notice any unusual or unexpected sounds that may be present, or the absence of expected sounds. We refer to these auditory perceptions as *signs suggestive of falsification*. If such signs are not perceived, it is not likely that the authenticity of the tape will be questioned. Signs suggestive of falsification may be the result of actual falsification, as will be discussed in Chapter 3. However, they may also arise from the operation of innocuous mechanisms. An *innocuous mechanism* is an undesired, naturally occurring event or condition that may affect the tape or its perceptual interpretation.

The various auditory signs suggestive of falsification are, for convenience, divided into six categories. These are labeled gaps, transients, fades, equipment sounds, extraneous voices, and information inconsistencies. In this chapter, we will discuss each category and give examples of how the signs could be produced by innocuous mechanisms. The chapter concludes with a discussion of the avoidability of some of these mechanisms.

The techniques used to examine tapes are applicable only to the extent to which information about the making of the tapes is available. In an ideal situation, all components of the recording system are available for examination and are as they were at the time the tape was made, the interconnections among these components are known, and details relating to the manner in which the system was operated can be provided. As the information available is diminished from this ideal, even the most powerful analysis techniques become inapplicable, and the examination may prove inconclusive. These and other problems will be discussed in Chapter 5.

The need for solutions to the problems associated with forensic examinations is likely to increase with continued use of tapes as evidentiary materials. Both short-term and long-term solutions are needed; some possible solutions are outlined in Chapter 6. It is the existence of these problems that undermines the use of tapes as evidence and that are the concern of this report.

B. CATEGORIES OF SIGNS SUGGESTIVE OF FALSIFICATION

1. Gaps

A *gap* in a recording is a segment in which the character of the recorded material changes abruptly for no apparent reason. The duration of a gap can range from thousandths of a second (i.e., a period too short to be noticed) to virtually the entire running time of the tape. A gap can contain silence, hum, buzzing sounds, etc.

A gap can be generated in a variety of ways. It can be the result of an intermittent connection somewhere in the recording system caused by an equipment malfunction or a poorly made connection. A gap will occur in the recording of a conversation that is being transmitted by radio to a remote recorder whenever the strength of the received radio signal falls below some minimum level. This type of gap will contain either silence if the receiver is equipped with a squelch circuit or static noises if it is not so equipped. A gap can occur in a telephone recording that is started automatically when the receiver is lifted and stopped when it is replaced. A failure of the control switch to operate properly may cause the recording to begin or end in mid conversation.

2. Transients

Transients are abrupt sounds of short duration such as clicks, pops, thumps, etc. They usually last less than one-tenth of a second and frequently less than one-hundredth of a second. Popularly, transients are associated with tape splices. While only a poorly made splice will produce such a sound, this association is one reason why the perception of a transient often suggests falsification. A second reason for classifying transients as suspicious sounds derives from an innocuous mechanism. A large number of tape recorders generate transients at the start of a recording and also at the end. Consequently, transients could be taken as an indication of an interruption of the recording process and consequently of a time lapse between the recordings just before and just after the transients.

There are numerous other innocuous causes of transients. Most common is the switching on or off of an electrical device while the recording is being made. Electric power transients are particularly apparent when the recorder is connected to the same power line as the device that is being switched, and when the device draws considerable current (for example, an air conditioner). It also is possible for a recorder to pick up the transient produced when a switch arcs. There are several other common sources of transients. In the case of telephone taps, there can be random click sounds on the telephone line. When a conversation is being transmitted by radio to a remote receiver, there is always the possibility of pickup of radio-frequency transients.

A much less frequent cause of clicks, but one that can be more troublesome to explain, is an intermittent connection. Since clicks caused by intermittencies will be accompanied by gaps in the recorded conversation, the combination is very likely to raise questions about the authenticity of the tape.

3. Fades

A *fade* is a substantial reduction in the strength of the recorded material. The reduction may reach the point where part of the speech becomes unintelligible. A fade becomes a gap when the strength of the recording drops abruptly below audibility. Fades can result from a decrease in battery voltage in a battery powered tape recorder. They can be caused by a variety of equipment malfunctions or poor connections. Fades that are caused by equipment malfunctions sometimes are accompanied by clicks at their beginning and end. Such a fade is second only to a gap in arousing suspicion about the authenticity of a tape.

4. Equipment Sounds

Equipment sounds are sounds that can occur during the making of a recording and that arise from the operation of the equipment. For example, sometimes a sound with a rapidly increasing pitch is heard at the point at which a recording stops. A similar sound with a rapidly decreasing pitch can sometimes be heard at the start of a recording. A junction between two adjacent recordings can exhibit a pair of such sounds that may suggest a splice to an untrained listener. In some recording situations, one of the parties to a conversation carries a microphone hidden under a garment. If the garment is allowed to contact the microphone and rub against it, a noise will be recorded.

Other equipment sounds commonly encountered are hum, whistles, and static. Hum is derived from the power line. It can be picked up by an unshielded or ungrounded microphone cable or telephone-tap cable. It can be generated by a faulty component inside a recorder that is powered by the line. Hum can become buzz for some types of circuit malfunctions or when there are periodic sharp disturbances on the power line.

Whistling sounds can be generated by oscillations inside a malfunctioning recording system. For speech that is transmitted by radio, whistles can be caused by pickup of a second transmitter at a frequency that is very close to the desired one.

Static can occur when a signal transmitted by radio is marginal in strength at the receiver. This occurs frequently in practical situations whenever there is a metallic object of substantial size between the transmitter and the receiver. Such an object can be, for example, the wire mesh in the wall of a building, a steel beam, or a truck that passes between the transmitter and a car in which the receiver is located.

5. Extraneous Voices

An *extraneous voice* heard on a tape is the voice of a person who appears to have been as close to the microphone as were the primary talkers. The *primary talkers* are the parties whose speech it was desired to record. Extraneous voices usually are heard in conversations recorded in public places such as bars, restaurants, and hotel lobbies. How close to a microphone a talker appears to be depends on the strength of the direct sound of the voice and the strength of the echoes of the voice. In a room with many echoes, an extraneous talker would have to be almost as close to the microphone as are the primary talkers to appear to have been among them. Conversely, in a relative echo-free room (e.g., one that is carpeted and that has drapes on the walls and sound absorbing tile on the ceiling), an extraneous talker whose voice was loud enough could be perceived as being in the same region as the primary talkers even though he was much farther from the microphone.

Extraneous voices are signs suggestive of falsification for several reasons. If they are loud enough, they can obscure the speech of a primary talker. A few words or fragments of words spoken by an extraneous talker can interlace with those of a talker in a way that affects the meaning of his statements without it being apparent that two people are speaking. This is the case especially when the voices of the two talkers are moderately similar. Finally, as will be discussed below, one of the primary talkers may not recall hearing a particular extraneous voice during the conversation that was recorded. He may thereupon suspect and charge that the tape had been altered.

6. Information Inconsistencies

An *information inconsistency* exists when the content of a recording differs from the statements, sounds, or events recalled by one of the primary talkers. The perceived difference can be the absence of words or statements that are recalled to have been spoken, or the presence of unrecalled ones. It can be a difference between the sequence of statements on the tape and the sequence of statements as they are recalled to have been made. It can be the presence of background noises (such as music) or conditions (such as reverberation) not recalled to have been present at the time the conversation was held.

Unquestionably, an information inconsistency may be the result of tape falsification. However, it also may be the result of human error. Memory is a subjective human ability prone to selection, suppression, and distortion depending on the interests and motivation of the individual. Even when trying consciously to be objective and accurate, people seldom remember exactly what they or someone else said, or what background sounds were present at the time. When they are talking or when they are listening to another talker, people tend to concentrate on speech and ignore background sounds. Finally, a conversation on a tape that is preferred as evidence may have taken place months or years earlier, a time long enough for details of the conversation and of the conditions under which it was held to have faded from memory.

C. CLASSES OF INNOCUOUS MECHANISMS

The innocuous mechanisms referred to above can be divided into three classes: environmental, instrumental, and procedural. The first class is concerned with the conditions under which the recording was made, the second with the characteristics and frailties of the recording system, and the third with methods used by the parties who produced the recording.

1. Environmental Mechanisms

A list of typical environmental mechanisms would include items such as background noise sources, stray electric or magnetic fields, crossed wires on telephone lines, radio interference, and power-line irregularities. Mechanisms such as these are intrinsic to the place at which a recording is made, and so are not readily avoidable. Consequently, it may not be possible to avoid the signs suggestive of falsification that they produce. For example, a recording made of a long-distance telephone call relayed over a marginal radio link is likely to contain a variety of transient sounds, fades, unidentifiable voices, and miscellaneous background noises. Since environmental mechanisms are essentially unavoidable, the best that can be done is to anticipate the mechanisms that are likely to be present in a particular recording situation and select a time or location that minimizes their effects.

2. Instrumental Mechanisms

All recording systems can malfunction or fail as a result of aging of system components, normal wear of mechanical parts, poor system interconnections, mishandling, and many other causes. When the performance of a system deteriorates or when it malfunctions or fails, it is likely to produce signs suggestive of falsification. Some examples are malfunctions that produce noises such as buzzes, clicks, or pops; intermittent failures that generate gaps; faulty ground connections resulting in hum and other noises; and battery deteriorations that cause changes in the recording volume.

While it is not possible to avoid such mechanisms entirely, it is possible to reduce the chance that some of them will occur. An obvious step that can be taken is to thoroughly check out the recording system before it is put to use. Components of the system can be inspected for loose connections and tested for significant deviations from performance specification or for other signs of incipient failure. A complete checkout should account for the fact that no matter how thoroughly a system is tested, there is always a chance that some instrumental mechanisms could be overlooked. In order to reveal potential problems, a test recording should be made during a rehearsal in which the system is used in the same way as it will be when the conversation of interest is recorded. Precautions such as these would help greatly to reduce the incidence of equipment malfunction or equipment failure during the making of recordings.

3. Procedural Mechanisms

Procedural mechanisms are, for the most part, avoidable. They arise from carelessness and from poor recording techniques. While accidents cannot be avoided altogether, some precautions can be taken to reduce their likelihood. Many procedural mechanisms could be avoided if the recording techniques included some commonsense steps. The list supplied below illustrates some of the basic steps that should be followed. If they seem elementary or excessively obvious, it should be noted that they are based on the experience of the authors with tapes whose authenticity had been questioned.

Connections between system components should not be held in place by hand. Wherever possible, only brand new tape should be used to make a recording; if previously used tape must be used, it should be bulk erased.* Tape that contains splices should never be used. A recording should not be started or ended on non-magnetic leader tape. If a tape is rewound to check the recording, it should be advanced to a point well beyond that at which the recording ended before the next recording is made. Tapes should be labeled to identify their contents using permanent labels. After a recording has been completed, the tape should not be left on the recorder or lying about. Copies of a tape should not be made by use of high-speed duplicating equipment that may tear, stretch, or otherwise mangle tapes.

In the experience of the authors, procedural mechanisms were responsible for the majority of the signs suggestive of falsification that they have observed. Each such sign required a painstaking examination of the tape to establish the innocuous nature of its origin. Without such an examination, substantial doubt would have remained as to the authenticity of the tape and this might have prevented the tape from being admitted into evidence.

CHAPTER 3—THE FALSIFICATION OF TAPES

A. INTRODUCTION

The signs suggestive of falsification described in Chapter 2 can, of course, be the product of tape falsification. *Falsification* is the deliberate alteration of a tape so as to change either the audibility or the meaning of the recorded material. There are four basic types of tape falsification. These are, in order of increasing sophistication, deletion, obscuration, transformation, and synthesis. The first two types comprise methods for suppressing information; the

---

*Bulk erasure is a process that removes all magnetization caused by previous recording on a tape.

last two types comprise methods for creating information. In this chapter, we will describe each type and some of the related methods. We will consider the degree of skill and the kind of equipment required for each method to be described. The chapter concludes with a discussion of the ease of falsifying tapes.

B. TYPES OF TAPE FALSIFICATION

1. Deletion

The simplest and most direct way to falsify a tape is to *delete* the unwanted material. By delete we mean either remove physically a segment of the tape or destroy a portion of the recording. Either way, the unwanted material is totally and permanently eliminated from the altered tape.

Consider first the destruction of a portion of a recording. The easiest way to accomplish this is to mount the tape on a tape recorder, locate the start and end of the segment that contains the material to be deleted, and record silence onto that segment. This technique is popularly known as erasing the tape. When an erasure is made carefully, the altered recording can appear to the casual listener as though there had been a failure in the recording system. However, to accomplish this without leaving additional signs suggestive of falsification, such as clicks and an elevated noise level, a high degree of skill on the part of the forger is required.

A second way to destroy a portion of a recording is to use two electrically inter-connected tape machines, one to play back the tape and the other to record a copy of it. If, while the copy is being made, the connection between the two machines is opened during the playing of the unwanted portion, the effect on the copy will be the same as though the original recording system had been malfunctioning. However, a high level of skill and technical knowledge is required on the part of the forger to avoid leaving evidence that the resulting tape is a copy.

These methods of deletion are convenient to use when the portion of the recording to be destroyed is at least one second in duration. The destruction of shorter portions such as a word or a part of a word requires the use of professional tape machines operated by highly trained personnel. By contrast, the second approach to deletion, namely the physical removal of a segment of tape, can be used to delete much shorter portions of a recording. The equipment that is required to perform this kind of deletion consists of a demagnetized razor or scissors to cut out the selected segment of the tape,* and adhesive splicing tape to join the ends of the remaining segments. Although some skill is needed to make secure noise-free splices, it can be acquired with relatively little practice. To eliminate the physical evidence of a splice, the forger will usually make a copy of the altered tape, using two machines as described above.

There is a second way to achieve the effect of physical removal of a segment of tape. While copying the tape using two machines, the movement of the recording machine is stopped during playback of the unwanted segment. While this method avoids the need to cut and splice the tape, it can cause clicks to be recorded when the recording machine is stopped and restarted.

Both destruction of a portion of a recording and physical removal of a segment of tape carry with them intrinsic risks of detection. Destruction will leave an obvious gap in the recording. A skilled forger will seek to make the gap in such a way that it appears to have been caused by innocuous mechanisms. Physical removal can leave a click, especially if the tape contained a significant level of speech or background noise. There are methods for reducing the detectability of such clicks. However, these require equipment and techniques that are not generally available.

2. Obscuration

Obscuration is the weakening or distorting of recorded material with the objective of making all or a part of the recording unintelligible. This type of falsification would be used when it is desirable to avoid splices, clicks, and gaps. If it is done well, falsification involving obscuration is much more difficult to detect and prove than falsification involving deletion.

By far the easiest and most flexible approach to obscuration makes use of a tape-copying system of the kind described earlier. One method is to reduce the recording level during playback of the portion of the recording to be obscured. When this is done correctly, the copied speech will be loud enough to be audible but too weak to be intelligible. The effect will be the same as though the recording level had dropped spontaneously while the conversation was being recorded. Another method is to add noise to the weakened speech while the copy is being made. By selecting the type of noise properly, the forger can enhance the impression that the obscuration resulted from a failure of the recording system. For example, if the tape to be obscured was made on a tape recorder connected to the power line, the noise should be power-line hum. Similarly, if the tape was recorded over a radio link, the noise should be radio static.

---

*By using a demagnetized cutting tool, the forger avoids magnetizing the tape in the vicinity of the splice and thereby leaving evidence of the existence of the splice.

Whether or not noise is added, the forger must be very skillful to avoid leaving evidence that the resulting tape is a copy.

There is a method for obscuring a recording that does not require the making of a copy. This is to partially erase the recording. The procedure is similar to that used in ordinary erasure except that the tape is displaced from the erase head of the tape recorder and thus contacts only the record head. When the machine is operating in the record mode, the record head will partially erase the tape. At the same time, it will record on top of the residual recording any signal that may be applied to the machine. The major flaw of this method is that clicks are likely to be recorded at the start and end of the partial erasure. Moreover, unless the same machine that made the recording is used to obscure it, there will be detectable differences between the clear and the obscured portions of the recording.

3. Transformation

Transformation is a type of falsification in which portions of a recording are changed or rearranged so as to alter the meaning of the recorded material. The changes can be insertions or deletions of individual speech sounds or sequences of speech sounds. For example, removing the *nt* sequence in the word *wouldn't* reverses the meaning of the sentence, "He said he wouldn't do it." While the methods suitable for accomplishing transformation of a recording are similar to those used in deletion, they differ in two important ways. First, they differ in their objectives; whereas deletion is used to suppress information, transformation is used to change it. The second difference is that in deletion recorded material is only removed, while in transformation recorded material can be removed, inserted, or rearranged.

Unless transformation is done with great care, the resulting recording can seem unnatural, mechanical, or artificial. If a speech sound is to be inserted, it must first be obtained and copied from speech occurring elsewhere on the same recording. Depending on the nature of the insertion to be made, proper selection of the needed sounds may require a great deal of experience and a knowledge of acoustic phonetics. Moreover, care must be taken to insure that the background noise accompanying the sound to be copied is very similar to the noise in the region where the sound is to be inserted. Finally, it almost certainly will be necessary to make a copy of the altered tape in order to hide physical evidence of splicing. Thus, while transformation can be a powerful type of falsification, great care and skill are needed to minimize the risk of detection.

4. Synthesis

Falsification by *synthesis* is the generation of a recording that is wholly artificial. In accordance with this definition, synthesis can be accomplished by adding background sounds to a recording so as to simulate conditions that were not present at the time the recording was made. These might be restaurant sounds, automobile sounds, echoes, extraneous voices, and so on.

Synthesis also can be the generation of recorded statements that were never actually spoken. This method consists of the splicing together of words, syllables, and speech sounds that have been taken out of their original contexts and arranged in a meaningful way. The necessary speech materials are drawn from a library of speech recordings assembled for this purpose. To obtain natural intonation patterns, it is necessary to have available a substantial body of speech recordings from which to draw appropriate samples. Moreover, the source material must have negligible background noise so that there are no obvious discontinuities in the synthesized recording. A suitable background can be added, if desired, when the final copy is made.

The techniques and equipment used to synthesize recordings are similar to those used in obscuration and transformation, but the level of skill that is required is substantially greater. Because of the restrictions described above, it is extremely difficult to synthesize a recording containing more than a few sentences. On the other hand, it is relatively easy to add background noises to an existing speech recording and thereby alter the apparent circumstances under which it was made. In either case, there is always the risk that a careful examination will expose this type of falsification.

C. EASE OF FALSIFYING TAPES

A forger needs a few pieces of relatively inexpensive and unsophisticated equipment, some skill in splicing and copying tapes, and only a few hours time to perform a superficially convincing falsification. On the other hand, a highly skilled forensic examiner who is an expert in the fields of tape recording, signal analysis, and speech communication, using the best available analysis equipment, can take weeks and even months to establish with reasonable certainty the fact that a tape has been falsified. The advantage, in terms of effort, time, and cost is clearly with the forger.

An example will be useful to emphasize the point. To perform deletion by splicing, the forger will need tape splicing equipment and one or possibly two high-quality tape recorders. He can readily rent this equipment for the one or two days he is likely to need them. Since the forger is likely to be working in his own interest, his services are, in effect, free. The forensic examiner must use special-purpose laboratory equipment the total cost of which can run to tens of thousands of dollars. He himself must possess the highest degree of technical knowledge and ingenuity if he is to be effective at his work. Thus, his services are likely to be expensive, particularly if the examination of the tape is protracted.

The forger has one additional advantage. Because a competent forensic examiner must be trained in several scientific disciplines, master a variety of technical arts, have access to the necessary equipment, and be available for the time required to conduct an examination, the potential forgers greatly outnumber the competent forensic examiners. This disparity increases the probability that a falsified tape will never be examined.

CHAPTER 4—ANALYTICAL APPROACH TO THE DETECTION OF TAPE FALSIFICATION

A. INTRODUCTION

The purpose of this chapter is to describe an analytical approach to the problem of detecting forgeries in the realm of magnetic tapes. This approach was developed by the authors and five of their colleagues during the recent Watergate investigation and has since been applied in numerous other legal cases. It represents the current state of the art of tape authentication.

1. Background and Philosophy

Many scientific tools and procedures are used in the forensic examination of a tape. Typically, the tape is subjected to a series of tests that are designed to detect certain unusual and unexpected conditions. If such conditions are not detected, however, the forensic examiner cannot conclude that the tape is authentic. A well done forgery may remain undisclosed because another test, which would have disclosed it, has not been performed. The only allowable conclusion is that the particular examination revealed no evidence of falsification.

A different precaution applies if unusual or unexpected conditions are detected. Some of these conditions may have been produced by innocuous mechanisms (see Chapter 2) and must be identified as such. This task requires considerable experience and judgment on the part of the forensic examiner.

Any remaining conditions constitute evidence that the tape under examination has been tampered with.

These circumstances do not differ greatly from those prevailing in other fields of forensic work. In the fine arts, for example, it is impossible to prove that a painting was created by a particular artist. At least in principle, a forgery painted by a skilled contemporary of the artist can elude modern detection methods. Also, not all unusual or unexpected conditions detected during an examination indicate fraud. Some of them may be the result of excessive handling, an unfavorable climate, or restoration efforts.

The results obtained in a forensic examination may be given a probabilistic interpretation. While negative test results do not rule out the possibility that the examined item is a forgery, they suggest that the probability of this being the case is rather small. If positive test results are obtained and all of them can be easily related to innocuous events, the probability of fraud is also very small. But any positive test results that cannot be accounted for in this manner are almost certainly indicative of falsification.

An inherent limitation of the analytical approach is the inability of scientific tests to distinguish between intentional and accidental falsifications. In a strict sense, not all falsifications are deliberate forgeries. Accidents involving magnetic tapes can occur without anyone's knowledge. Even when someone knows that an accident has occurred, the accident is often unreported and the forensic examiner is therefore unaware of this innocuous mechanism. Because the distinction between intentional and accidental falsifications is important from the legal point of view, the forensic examiner must refrain from speculating about this matter. It is the function of the judge and jury to evaluate the significance of recorded conversations and other information available in the case.

2. From the Acoustic Sources to the Examiner's Ears

When the forensic examiner interprets his findings, he inevitably ponders about events and processes that represent specific early stages in the generation of the tape under study. It is convenient to think of these stages as forming a complete information path that extends from the acoustic sources to the examiner's ears. A block diagram of this information path is shown in Figure 1.

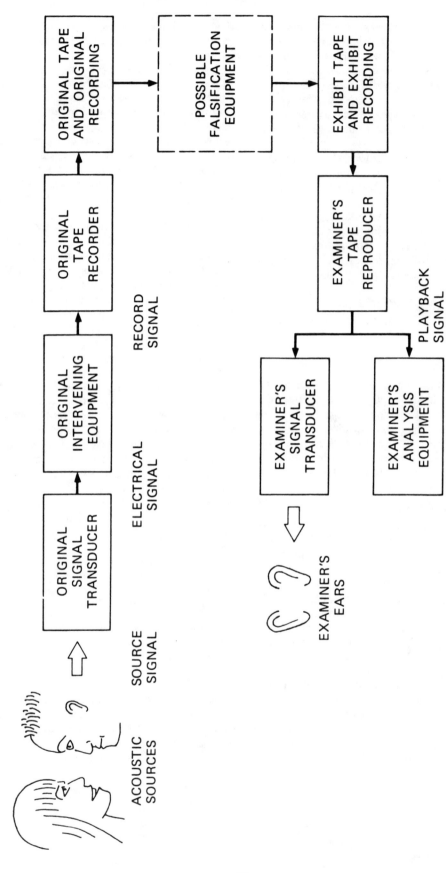

FIGURE 1   BLOCK DIAGRAM OF INFORMATION PATH FROM ACOUSTIC SOURCES TO EXAMINER'S EARS

Usually, two kinds of *acoustic sources* operate simultaneously. The first kind of acoustic source emanates intelligence that is considered worth preserving. An example is a speaking person. The second kind of acoustic source emanates unwanted information and noise. Common examples are a background music system, a group of yelling children, and a jet airplane. Although the second kind of acoustic source is of little interest to most people, it plays an important role in forensic work. The combined sound output from both kinds of acoustic sources is called the *source signal*.

The *original signal transducer* is the electro-mechanical device that was used to convert the source signal into an *electrical signal*. Examples of such devices are a high-quality dynamic microphone, a carbon-granule telephone transmitter, and a miniature microphone designed for surreptitious use. Because of certain limitations of the original signal transducer, the electrical signal may differ slightly from the source signal.

The electrical signal is usually processed by some electronic equipment referred to as the *original intervening equipment*. Examples of such equipment are an amplifier, an induction pick-up device attached to a telephone set, and a miniature radio transmitter and receiver. The specifications and use of the original intervening equipment determine to what extent the electrical signal is degraded by noise and distortion as it is processed. The processed electrical signal is called the *record signal*.

The *original tape recorder* is the machine that was used to capture and preserve the record signal. It may be a broadcast-quality tape recorder, a portable cassette tape recorder, or a tape recorder designed for dictation. Many types of tape recorders are in common use, each type having particular features and characteristics that are of interest to the forensic examiner. The physical tape used with the original tape recorder is called the *original tape*, and the magnetic information written on the original tape by the original tape recorder is called the *original recording*.

After the original recording has been made, the original tape may fall into the hands of a forger. Using a variety of tools and techniques available to him, the forger can falsify the original recording and thereby change the meaning of the recorded material. Examples of *possible falsification equipment* will be given below.

The *exhibit tape* is the physical tape that is submitted to the forensic examiner. It may be the original tape, a portion of the original tape, or an entirely different tape supplied by a forger. The magnetic information written on the exhibit tape is called the *exhibit recording*. If no forger was involved, the exhibit recording will be the original recording. Otherwise, it may be an incomplete version or a rearrangement of the original recording.

In the course of the forensic examination, the exhibit recording is played back on the *examiner's tape reproducer*. Whenever possible, this is a high-quality machine that introduces an absolute minimum of noise and distortion. The examiner's tape reproducer must be technically compatible with the exhibit tape and the exhibit recording. The output of the examiner's tape reproducer is an electrical signal called the *playback signal*.

The characteristics of the playback signal may be studied in detail by means of the *examiner's analysis equipment*. An instrument known as an oscillograph is particularly useful for this purpose. It provides a permanent graphic record of how the playback signal varies as a function of time. Another useful instrument is a spectrum analyzer, which shows how the energy of the playback signal is distributed over the audio frequency range. The examiner's analysis equipment includes not only commercially available instruments but also apparatus that has been especially designed and constructed to perform unusual measurements.

The playback signal may also be converted into sound by means of the *examiner's signal transducer*. This can be either a loudspeaker system or a pair of high-quality earphones. Perhaps the best instruments that can be used in the examination of an exhibit tape are the examiner's ears. The experienced forensic examiner is well trained as a critical listener. He can easily detect subtle changes in an exhibit recording that may elude the most sophisticated electronic detector.

Two examples of possible falsification equipment are given in Figure 2. Example 1 shows an arrangement of equipment suitable for falsifying an original recording by obscuration (see Chapter 3). The original recording is played back continuously on the *forger's tape reproducer*, which is probably a high-quality machine. During playback, the output of the forger's tape reproducer and the output of the *forger's noise generator* are carefully blended, using the *forger's mixer*, so as to obscure all or only certain parts of the original recording. The composite signal is simultaneously recorded with the *forger's tape recorder*.

If the forger has access to the original tape recorder, he will use this machine because it produces recordings that closely resemble the original recording. Also, he will use a tape that closely resembles the original tape. Nevertheless, the exhibit tape and the exhibit recording he delivers almost always contain some detectable signs of falsification.

Example 2 of Figure 2 shows how an original recording can be falsified by transformation. In this example, the forger edits the original tape by cutting and splicing it. He may thereby remove certain parts of the original recording and change the sequence of other parts. The resulting rearrangement of the original recording is then played back on the forger's tape reproducer and simultaneously copied with the forger's tape recorder (or the original tape recorder, if it is available to the forger). This procedure provides a splice-free exhibit tape containing an artifically created exhibit recording. However, because the forger must make compromises during the editing operation, the forensic examiner can usually determine that such an exhibit recording is a forgery.

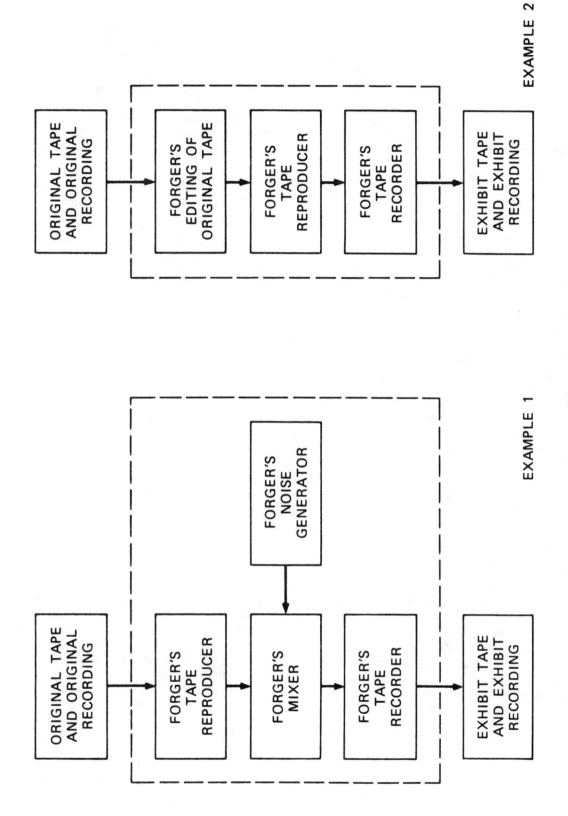

FIGURE 2   TWO EXAMPLES OF POSSIBLE FALSIFICATION EQUIPMENT

B. THE SEARCH FOR EVIDENCE OF FALSIFICATION

The forensic examiner deals with this basic question: Is the playback signal a complete and accurate reproduction of the source signal, allowing for some minor deviations that are inherently introduced by the original signal transducer, the original intervening equipment, and the original tape recorder? Since the source signal is not available for comparison with the playback signal, this question cannot be answered directly. The answer must necessarily be inferred from answers to related questions concerning observable and measurable properties of the exhibit tape and the exhibit recording.

Four such questions will be stated and discussed in the following sections of this chapter. These questions are of the form: Are certain properties of the exhibit tape or the exhibit recording consistent with established facts or reasonable assumptions about a specific earlier point in the information path shown in Figure 1? No matter what test the forensic examiner applies, any inconsistency that is not attributable to an innocuous mechanism constitutes evidence that falsification equipment was used. Such evidence, in turn, implies that the playback signal is not a complete and accurate reproduction of the source signal.

In discussing each of the four questions, several applicable measurement procedures or detection methods will be described. These are examples of frequently used forensic tools; they have been chosen to illustrate the scope of the forensic examiner's work. No effort is made to provide an exhaustive catalog of available detection methods.

1. Are the Properties of the Exhibit Tape Consistent With What Is Known or Can Reasonably Be Assumed About the Original Tape?

This question refers to the physical properties of the exhibit tape, including its length and thickness, the type of base material (acetate or polyester) and emulsion (red oxide, black oxide, high-output formula, etc.) used in its manufacture, and its condition with respect to wear and the presence of splices.

These physical properties of the exhibit tape can be compared against available facts or reasonable assumptions about the original tape. For example, if the exhibit tape measures 550 feet long and 1.5 mil thick and it is spooled on a 5 inch reel, an inconsistency has been uncovered because 1.5 mil thick tape that is commercially spooled on a 5 inch reel is nominally 600 feet long (the manufacturer's tolerance is only a few feet).

It is obvious that the more that is known about the original tape, the more fully can this question be answered. Information provided by the user of the original tape may be incomplete or even incorrect and should always be confirmed by others before it is considered factual. Contradicted and disputed information must be disregarded.

2. Are the Properties of the Exhibit Recording Consistent With What Is Known or Can Reasonably Be Assumed About the Original Tape Recorder and the Original Recording?

The exhibit recording has several properties that reflect the type of tape recorder on which it was made and the manner in which the tape recorder was operated.

One of these properties of the exhibit recording is the width of the *magnetic track* written by the tape recorder. The track written on a tape can be made visible by a technique known as *magnetic development*. A section of tape is immersed in a volatile fluid containing magnetic particles in suspension. As the particles drift through the fluid, some of them become fixed to the tape by magnetic attraction. When the tape is removed from the developing bath, any fluid remaining on the tape evaporates and the distribution of the particles fixed to the tape becomes visible. This distribution conforms in detail to the magnetic field variations written on the tape.

Some tape recorders write across the entire width of the tape (these are called full-track tape recorders), while others write a narrow track along one edge of the tape (these are called half-track tape recorders). Still other tape recorders write two narrow tracks simultaneously (these are called two-track or stereo tape recorders). By examining the tracks on a developed section of the exhibit tape, the forensic examiner can identify the type of tape recorder on which the exhibit recording was made.

Another tape-recorder signature often found in an exhibit recording is a frequency modulation of tones present in the background noise. This property of a recording is commonly known as *flutter*. The tones may have been produced by an acoustic source, in the original intervening equipment, or in the electronics of the original tape recorder.

Most inexpensive tape recorders cannot record tones accurately because any rotating part that is slightly eccentric will cause minute speed variations. During playback of the recording on a laboratory-quality tape reproducer operating at constant speed, each tone will vary in frequency by an amount that is exactly proportional to the diameter of the eccentric rotating part. Since different types of tape recorders employ different mechanisms, flutter measurements often allow the forensic examiner to identify the type of tape recorder involved.

Factual information about the original tape recorder is usually easy to obtain. In many cases, the original tape recorder can be made available to the forensic examiner for experimentation. He can prepare test recordings and compare these with the exhibit recording, checking for consistency of the properties under discussion. In other cases, the original tape recorder is not available, but some of its design features and characteristics are known. Cases in which nothing is known about the original tape recorder are rare.

Whenever a tape recorder is started in the record mode or stopped while in the record mode, *magnetic marks* are written on a tape that is threaded on the machine. These marks can be made visible by magnetic development and used to determine how an exhibit recording was created.

Starting and stopping a tape recorder produces different marks. In a recording made by stopping and restarting the tape recorder several times without rewinding the tape, each start mark is followed by a stop mark and each stop mark is followed by a start mark or unrecorded tape. On the other hand, in a recording made by stopping the tape recorder, rewinding a portion of the tape, and then restarting the tape recorder, there may be two successive start marks and two successive stop marks. By studying the sequence of start marks and stop marks, the forensic examiner can tell whether the exhibit recording was made in a single pass through the tape recorder or by recording new material over a previous recording.

The results of this analysis are checked for consistency with available factual information on how the original recording was made. For example, if the exhibit recording is found to end with a start mark (instead of a stop mark) and the original recording is known to have been made in a single pass through the original tape recorder, there is an inconsistency suggesting that the last part of the original recording was subsequently deleted by erasure.

3. Are the Properties of the Exhibit Recording Consistent With What Is Known or Can Reasonably Be Assumed About the Original Signal Transducer and the Original Intervening Equipment?

Various properties of the exhibit recording reflect the type of signal transducer and the type of electronic equipment that were involved in its creation. These properties are measured by analyzing the playback signal using conventional methods of audio-signal analysis.

Each type of signal transducer (condenser microphone, dynamic microphone, telephone transmitter, etc.) produces a slightly different electrical signal from the same acoustic input signal. The characteristic sound quality associated with a particular type of signal transducer is often recognized in critical listening. Measurements of the electrical signal, including bandwidth and distortion measurements, may be used to confirm the aural identification. A speech signal picked up with a telephone transmitter is typically more restricted in bandwidth and more distorted than a speech signal picked up with a dynamic microphone.

The exhibit recording is also affected by the type of electronic equipment that was used between the signal transducer and the tape recorder. As mentioned earlier, the electronic equipment may introduce a characteristic background noise containing tones. For example, a high-gain microphone amplifier may pick up from its power supply several harmonics of the power frequency. Another example of a characteristic background noise is the hum picked up by a suction-cup device used to record telephone conversations. If a radio link intervenes between the signal transducer and the tape recorder, as is the case with a wireless microphone, the recording may be degraded by occasional interference from other sources of radio-frequency energy.

It is usually possible to obtain some factual information about the original signal transducer and the original intervening equipment. This information is used to interpret the results of the signal analysis performed on the exhibit recording. Any unexplainable inconsistency constitutes evidence that falsification equipment was involved in the creation of the exhibit recording.

4. Are the Properties of the Exhibit Recording Consistent With What Is Known or Can Reasonably Be Assumed About the Acoustic Sources?

The properties of the exhibit recording referred to in this question are sounds and sound patterns that represent acoustic events. These properties are monitored primarily by critical listening, although electrical measurements are sometimes helpful in the analysis of details.

While listening to the exhibit recording, particular attention is paid to background sounds that could not have been produced by actual acoustic sources. An example is the sudden cessation of the sound of ringing church bells. Also of interest are background sounds that are physically possible but extremely unlikely in view of some general knowledge about the recording site. Examples of such sounds are an abrupt change in the level of traffic noise and an echo during one part of a dialogue supposedly recorded outdoors. The presence of these kinds of sounds suggests strongly that the exhibit recording is a forgery.

The amount of available factual information about the acoustic sources varies from case to case. Occasionally, all acoustic sources that were active when the original recording was made can be identified and data relating to their acoustical environment are available. In most cases, however, only the primary talkers and some of the acoustic sources of background noise can be identified. Usually, only one of the background noise sources can be studied retrospectively. Common examples of such acoustic sources include power tools, motor vehicles, air conditioners, table radios, and stereo phonographs. Unfortunately, there are many cases in which little is known about the acoustic sources and even less about their acoustical environment.

The forensic examiner can never be sure that the playback signal accurately reflects the entire time interval during which the acoustic sources were active, without omission of parts of this interval, without change in the sequence of parts of this interval, and without insertion of parts of other intervals. But he can easily demonstrate that the playback signal is fraudulent if he finds an inconsistency between the results of his analysis of sound patterns and knowledge of or reasonable assumptions about the acoustic sources.

C. TWO HYPOTHETICAL CASES ILLUSTRATING THE APPLICATION OF THE ANALYTICAL APPROACH

In order to illustrate the application of the analytical approach, we will describe two hypothetical cases in which falsification equipment was used. The falsification techniques involved are those shown in Figure 2. Of course, the forensic examiner does not know what, if anything, is contained in the dashed outlines of this figure. In each case, he is given an exhibit tape and certain facts about the acoustic sources, the original signal transducer, the original intervening equipment, the original tape recorder, the original tape, and the original recording.

1. The First Case

The forensic examiner knows that a long-distance telephone call has been recorded using an induction pick-up device attached to the caller's telephone set and a portable tape recorder. This equipment is made available to him for experimentation. The exhibit recording contains a loud hum and appears to be unusually noisy, even for a long-distance call. Both voices are weak and difficult to understand, and in some parts of the recording the voice of the called party is unintelligible. It seems that this voice becomes unintelligible whenever a particular topic comes up in the conversation. For this reason, the exhibit tape has been submitted for examination.

The findings in this case are as follows: Since no information is available about the original tape, the physical properties of the exhibit tape are of little interest. The exhibit tape is of a kind that could be used with the original tape recorder furnished. In fact, the track width of the exhibit recording matches the track width of a test recording made on the original tape recorder. Flutter measurements taken on the exhibit recording are inconclusive. However, the rate at which signal energy falls off at the upper and lower frequency limits is much greater for the exhibit recording than for a test recording of other telephone conversations. On the basis of further examination of the exhibit recording, there is no reason to believe that telephone equipment and an induction pick-up device were not involved in its creation. There are no recognizable background sounds to be analyzed.

Although the primary task of the forensic examiner is to expose inconsistencies that are not attributable to innocuous mechanisms, his work is not complete until he has interpreted his findings and arrived at a reasonable concept of how a forgery was accomplished.

The one inconsistency uncovered in this case, namely the difference in the rate of signal-energy falloff, provides a clue that the original tape recorder was used twice in the creation of the exhibit recording. This clue leads directly to the speculation that the exhibit recording is an altered copy of the original recording. Furthermore, having observed the high noise level and the weakness of the voices, the forensic examiner will probably surmise that the exhibit recording was created in the manner shown in Example 1 of Figure 2.

Before expressing an opinion, however, the forensic examiner will want to make sure that his hypothesis can explain all of the results obtained. He tests his hypothesis by simulating what he believes was the work of the forger. The simulation is usually incomplete, especially with respect to details, because the forensic examiner does not have control over all of the variables that existed when the forgery was carried out.

2. The Second Case

It is known that the president of a bank met with several contractors in his conference room to discuss their proposals for a new building. One of the contractors recorded the discussion by means of a portable tape recorder with a built-in microphone, which he had placed in front of him on the conference table. In a later dispute with the bank, this contractor claimed that the job had been promised to him during the president's conference and played a tape to support his argument. The bank charged that the tape has been tampered with.

The forensic examiner has been given a supply of unused original tapes and the original tape recorder. He has also inspected the bank president's conference room, which is furnished with a large conference table surrounded by swivel chairs, two side tables, a small bar, and a refrigerator with an ice-cube maker.

A thorough analysis of the materials and facts obtained in this case yields the following results. The physical properties of the exhibit tape are consistent with those of the unused original tapes. There are no splices in the exhibit tape. Only two magnetic marks are found in the exhibit recording; there is a start mark at the beginning of the recording and a stop mark at the end. These two marks are consistent with marks in a test recording that was made on the original tape recorder. Flutter measurements confirm that the exhibit recording was made on the original tape recorder, but they also suggest that the original tape recorder may have been used twice in the creation of the exhibit recording.

The speech heard in the exhibit recording has about the same sound quality as speech recorded for test purposes, using the original tape recorder and its built-in microphone. A distinctive rumbling sound can be heard in the background at irregular intervals throughout the exhibit recording. The source of this sound has been identified as the refrigerator in the conference room; the sound is produced when newly made ice cubes fall into a tray. In the conference room, the sound does not occur more often than once every 15 or 20 minutes. According to the manufacturer of the refrigerator, it takes at least ten minutes to freeze new ice cubes. In the exhibit recording, however, two occurrences of the sound are separated by only three minutes.

The background sounds heard in the exhibit recording are thus inconsistent with knowledge about their acoustic source. This inconsistency is a primary clue that the exhibit recording is not the original recording. If there were splices in the exhibit tape, then the exhibit recording could be a rearrangement of portions of the original recording, prepared by cutting and splicing the original tape. Some portions of the original recording could be missing and other portions could be transposed in time so as to change the meaning of the recorded material. But since there are no splices in the exhibit tape, the forensic examiner will infer that the exhibit recording is a copy of such an edited rearrangement, made on the original tape recorder.

This interpretation is supported by the flutter measurements, which allowed for the possibility that the original tape recorder was used twice in the creation of the exhibit recording. The hypothesized falsification technique is shown in Example 2 of Figure 2.

CHAPTER 5—PROBLEMS IN THE PRACTICAL APPLICATION OF THE ANALYTICAL APPROACH

A. INTRODUCTION

The analytical approach described in Chapter 4 has a good theoretical foundation and considerable potential for detecting even relatively subtle falsifications. However, when it is applied in actual cases, several kinds of problems become apparent. Various methodological limitations are encountered by the forensic examiner in the course of his work. In addition, there are problems relating to the analytical approach in general that burden the employers of forensic examiners and ultimately the courts. Many of these problems will be identified and discussed in this chapter.

B. BASIC PROBLEM AREAS

There are five basic problem areas. The problems in any one area are largely independent of the problems in the other areas, but all problem areas are usually represented in a given case.

1. Scarcity of Factual Information

The effectiveness of the analytical approach depends almost entirely on the availability of factual information about the acoustic sources, the original signal transducer, the original intervening equipment, the original tape recorder, the original tape, and the original recording. In most real cases, many claims and counterclaims are made with respect to these items, but only a few facts are available to the forensic examiner. These facts are often insufficient to interpret the results of the examination. Critical measurements performed on the exhibit tape and the exhibit recording cannot be properly evaluated because of the absence of reference criteria.

For example, in order to evaluate a measurement of the width of the magnetic track written on an exhibit tape, certain factual information about the original tape recorder must be available. If it is not known whether the original tape recorder was a full-track machine, a half-track machine, or a stereo machine, the measurement of track width is useless. Similarly, in order to evaluate a flutter measurement obtained from an exhibit recording, the internal mechanism of the original tape recorder must be known to the forensic examiner. In the absence of factual information about the original tape recorder, the forensic examiner is severely handicapped in his effort to establish whether or not falsification equipment was involved in the creation of the exhibit recording.

2. Restrictions on Measurements

It is often impossible to perform certain desirable measurements on the exhibit tape or the exhibit recording because of unfortunate technical circumstances. Such restrictions on measurements are especially frustrating when the relevant factual information needed to interpret the measurements is readily available. Two examples will serve to clarify this problem area.

Among the most useful measurements that can be taken on the exhibit recording are the dimensions of the magnetic marks at the beginning and end of the recording. These dimensions identify more specifically the type of tape recorder on which the exhibit recording was made than the width of the magnetic track. Therefore, they often allow the forensic examiner to rule out the possibility that the exhibit recording was made on the original tape recorder even though the track width is consistent. When the exhibit tape is contained in a cassette rather than on a reel, there may be no magnetic marks at the beginning and end of the exhibit recording. Cassette tapes have short lengths of non-magnetic leader tape spliced to the beginning and end of the magnetic tape, and cassette tape recorders are commonly started and stopped while this leader tape is in contact with the record and erase heads of the machine.

Flutter measurements are another means of identifying the type of tape recorder on which the exhibit recording was made. They are often sufficiently unique to disclose the involvement of falsification equipment when other test results are negative. However, flutter measurements can be taken only if the exhibit recording contains tones in the background noise. Furthermore, regardless of their source, the tones must have been steady in both amplitude and frequency when the original recording was made. Most exhibit recordings contain no tones, and many of those that do are unsuitable for flutter measurements because the tones are unsteady.

3. Availability of Analysis Equipment

Typically, the forensic examiner does not have access to all of the analysis equipment that would be necessary to perform all of the measurements desired in a particular case. While the tools for magnetic development are clearly within his reach, an oscillograph and a spectrum analyzer with characteristics appropriate for the intended use are more difficult to acquire. Very few commercial instruments can be used to perform flutter measurements; these instruments are very expensive and are therefore not generally available. There are some advantages to performing certain measurements with the aid of a digital computer, but the requirements for storage of the exhibit recording in digital form are enormous and exclude this approach for most forensic examiners who have access to a computer.

The examination of an exhibit tape is almost always limited by the availability of suitable analysis equipment. Consequently, the forensic examiner must improvise with whatever equipment is available to him so that the measurements deemed most important for the case at hand can be carried out. He may see a need to modify existing equipment or to construct special-purpose equipment to his own specifications. In the Watergate case, for example, it was necessary to check lengthy exhibit tapes for possible thermal splices, which can be nearly invisible. A novel tape sensor was designed and built to perform this task automatically; the device was found to be so sensitive that it responded to crayon markings on the back of the tape. Such special-purpose equipment can be realized only if the forensic examiner has access to laboratory and production facilities.

4. Competence of Forensic Examiner

The competent forensic examiner posesses a special blend of traits: He has the necessary training, objectivity, ingenuity, and patience to pursue his work in strict compliance with the scientific method. Using all available facts, he first constructs several alternative hypotheses concerning the creation of the exhibit recording. Then he proceeds to test each hypothesis by performing appropriate experiments. This is a reiterative process with which he is very familiar.

In addition to his technical expertise, the forensic examiner is able to evaluate the credibility of information offered to him. This trait is essential because the forensic examiner must determine for himself what information he will regard as factual. If he is too lenient, he will soon be confused in a wealth of conflicting "facts"; if he is too sceptical, he will be unable to construct and test hypotheses. He knows from experience what criteria to apply in evaluating the probable truthfulness of each piece of information he receives.

Because the examination of tapes is a relatively new branch of forensic science, there are currently only a few competent forensic examiners in this field. The demand for examinations is already substantial, as judged from the many inquiries addressed to the authors, and it appears to be steadily increasing. A problem is therefore anticipated: If a case should come up when the competent forensic examiners are working on other cases or are otherwise unavailable, much less competent persons may be called upon. Inaccurate and misleading testimony has already been given in at least one case by a self-declared expert who was familiar with legal procedures but had no experience in examining tapes.

5. Time and Cost

After agreeing to work on a new case, the forensic examiner usually conducts a preliminary examination of the materials submitted to him. He reviews available facts, listens carefully to the exhibit recording, and takes a few simple measurements as he formulates an initial plan of action. Then he communicates with his employer and estimates what additional work would be required in order to reach a definite conclusion. Such a preliminary examination may take a few days; a thorough follow-up examination may easily take several months. Extensive examinations frequently hold up court schedules and thus delay the resolution of cases.

The cost of even a preliminary examination can be prohibitive to a defendant without funds. More detailed examinations are sometimes waived by a court because neither the prosecution nor the defense is able to underwrite the expenses involved. According to the author's experience, a routine examination may easily cost five thousand dollars. The examination of the Watergate tapes was the most expensive examination to date; it cost well over one hundred thousand dollars.

C. TWO ACTUAL CASES ILLUSTRATING A VARIETY OF PROBLEMS

Two actual cases will be described in order to illustrate some of the problems encountered in the practical application of the analytical approach. These cases are drawn from the author's experience.

1. The First Case

The forensic examiner was told that several telephone conversations have been recorded on a single tape by means of automatic recording equipment. Whenever a call was made or received on a particular telephone line, a control switch sensed a change in the electrical signal and started a tape recorder that was connected to the line. At the end of the call, the control switch turned the tape recorder off. There was no information on the kind of tape that had been used with this equipment. Two tape recorders were given to the forensic examiner; it was not known which of the two machines was the original tape recorder. The control switch was allegedly misplaced shortly after the equipment was disconnected.

The examination of the exhibit recording yielded inconclusive results. Neither measurements of magnetic marks nor flutter measurements allowed the forensic examiner to associate the exhibit recording with one of the two tape recorders furnished. If the measurements taken on the exhibit recording had been more distinctive, and if the forensic examiner had been more completely satisfied that the original tape recorder was indeed in his possession, then he might have been able to establish whether the exhibit recording contained evidence of falsification.

Each recorded telephone conversation was preceded by a peculiar chirping sound. These sounds could have been produced by automatic recording equipment of the kind described above. However, they could also have been produced by falsification equipment. A detailed analysis of the sounds provided no information as to which source was more likely. If the control switch had been available for use in simulation experiments, its electrical signature could have been obtained and compared with the results of the sound analysis. Under the prevailing circumstances, it was impossible to draw any conclusions with respect to the origin of the chirping sounds.

2. The Second Case

A conversation between a female undercover agent and two suspects, a man and a woman, has been recorded in a busy cocktail lounge. They were sitting at a table not far from a piano, which was being played intermittently. The agent was wired for sound; she had a miniature michrophone hidden in the ruffled colar of her dress and she wore a miniature radio transmitter. A radio receiver and a cassette tape recorder were being operated in an unmarked police car that was parked across the street from the cocktail lounge. When the case went to trial, the defense challenged the authenticity of the tape offered into evidence.

The exhibit recording was partly unintelligible. In addition to the voices of the agent and the two suspects, it contained a confusion of other voices, fragments of music played on a piano, and much noise. There were no background sounds that could be analyzed to determine whether they were consistent with knowledge about acoustic sources. Occasionally, there was an interval of complete silence, suggesting that a connection had been broken and reestablished. These interruptions were believed to have been caused by trucks passing in front of the cocktail lounge and momentarily obstructing the radio link.

All of the equipment used by the police was made available to the forensic examiner. In experimenting with the radio transmitter and receiver, the forensic examiner discovered that the radio channel used to make the original recording was assigned to several police radio stations. Whenever one of these stations went on the air, it interfered with test signals received from the miniature transmitter. This kind of interference could not be ruled out as a possible factor contributing to the poor quality of the exhibit recording.

No magnetic start mark was found at the beginning of the exhibit recording. The cassette tape recorder used to make the exhibit recording had been started on non-magnetic leader tape. Neither was there a magnetic stop mark at the end of the exhibit recording. The recorded material ended without a magnetic mark because the radio link had been broken before the tape recorder was switched off. A short interval of silence followed, and then there was a sequence of three brief extraneous recordings. Each extraneous recording began with a start mark and ended with a stop mark. One of the extraneous recordings had erased the delayed stop mark of the exhibit recording.

The contents of the extraneous recordings suggested that someone had inadvertently used the exhibit tape to demonstrate the operation of a tape recorder (not necessarily the original tape recorder). Because of this mishap, the forensic examiner was unable to determine whether the exhibit recording could have been made on the original tape recorder.

CHAPTER 6—SUMMARY, CONCLUSIONS, AND RECOMMENDATIONS

A. SUMMARY

In order to introduce a tape into evidence, an attorney must demonstrate to the satisfaction of the court that the material recorded on it is intelligible, that the talkers heard have been properly identified, and finally that the tape is authentic. Demonstrating the authenticity of the tape is usually the most difficult of these three tasks. Traditionally, *prima facie* authenticity is established by proving that no unauthorized person has had access to the tape from the time of its creation to the time it is offered into evidence. A log listing all persons who have handled the tape is prepared for this purpose, and the tape is officially sealed when it is submitted to the court. However, even if this procedure is followed, there may be grounds for challenging the authenticity of the tape.

A careful listening to the tape may reveal various signs suggesting that the tape has somehow been tampered with. These signs suggestive of falsification include gaps, transients, fades, equipment sounds, extraneous voices, and information incon-sistencies. The mere fact that such signs are observed does not constitute proof of fraudulent intervention. Many signs suggestive of falsification are caused by innocuous mechanisms. These include environmental mechanisms (e.g., background noise sources), instrumental mechanisms (e.g., equipment malfunctions), and procedural mechanisms (e.g., poor recording technique). In order to determine whether or not the tape has been falsified, it is often necessary to perform a detailed scientific examination.

There are four types of tape falsification. These are deletion, in which a segment of tape is physically removed or a portion of the recording is destroyed; obscuration, in which all or part of the recording is made unintelligible; transformation, in which portions of the recording are changed or rearranged; and synthesis, in which a totally artificial recording is generated. These four types of falsification encompass a large number of specific methods. It is relatively easy to falsify a tape because superficially undetectable alterations can be made with inexpensive and readily available equipment in the hands of a technically naive forger. Nevertheless, a falsified tape usually contains some residual signs of each step of its creation.

The forensic examiner uses an analytical approach to the detection of tape falsification. This approach provides theoretical guidelines for performing various scientific tests that are designed to expose any unusual or unexpected conditions in the tape being examined. If such conditions are detected, and if the forensic examiner cannot attribute them to innocuous mechanisms, he is forced to conclude that the tape has indeed been falsified. By means of simulation experiments, he may even be able to demonstrate exactly how the falsification was carried out. On the other hand, if no unusual or unexpected conditions are detected, the probability that the tape has been falsified is very low. The forensic examiner may conclude that the tape is authentic.

When the forensic examiner comes to this conclusion, he is stating a professional opinion and not a scientific fact. As an expert in several scientific disciplines, he is able to explain to the court what kind of tests he conducted and what his findings were. He is also able to explain the logic underlying his conclusion. However, because he cannot avoid making some assumptions, and because his tools of measurement are finite in number and inherently imperfect, his conclusion that a particular tape is authentic is always regarded as an opinion.

Unfortunately, there are many problems in the practical application of the analytical approach.

For example, the usefulness of the approach depends heavily on the availability of facts concerning the technical circumstances under which the tape was originally made. In most actual cases, factual information is extremely scarce. Other problems relate to restrictions on measurements, the availability of analysis equipment, the competence of the forensic examiner, and the time and cost of examinations. These problems seriously limit the practical application of the analytical approach. Many forensic examinations are therefore inconclusive and of no value to the courts that ordered them.

B. CONCLUSIONS

Tapes that are made for use in criminal investigations can be falsified, even by relatively unskilled persons, in ways that are superficially convincing. The necessary equipment is readily available, and the necessary techniques are easily learned. Because of the problems of forensic examination of tapes, it is likely that such alterations will go undetected. In fact, because of these problems, most of the tapes that require a competent and thorough examination to establish their authenticity will not receive one. While the number of such tapes is relatively small at this time, the potential exists for a substantial increase. Tapes that are made for evidentiary purposes usually contain signs suggestive of falsification, primarily because of the operation of innocuous mechanisms. These signs provide the bases for challenges to the authenticity of the tapes. Such challenges have been infrequent in the past. However, in the wake of the Watergate investigation, it has become common knowledge that tapes whose authenticity is questionable can be tested objectively by use of scientific methods of examination. As more challenges to the admission of tapes into evidence succeed, the challenging of the authenticity of tapes is bound to be encouraged. On the other hand, most challenged tapes are not submitted for examination. While those that are usually cannot be conclusively authenticated, neither can they be shown conclusively to have been falsified. Consequently, the temptation to falsify tapes also will be encouraged. Developments such as these obviously would undermine the use of tapes as evidentiary materials. To avoid them, solutions must be found for the problems of forensic examination of tapes.

There are four main sources of these problems: the number of tapes that can be challenged is greatly inflated by the incidence of signs suggestive of falsification that result from the operation of innocuous mechanisms; the ease with which tapes can be falsified makes it necessary to take seriously any such signs that can not be explained readily; the difficulty of performing forensic examinations limits the number of available competent examiners and the number of tapes they can examine; and the lack of technical information about the manner in which tapes are produced makes it difficult for a forensic examiner to achieve conclusive test results. By finding solutions that will eliminate these sources or at least reduce their significance, the problems of forensic examination of tapes can be alleviated.

C. RECOMMENDATIONS

Satisfactory resolution of the problems of forensic examination of tapes requires both near-term and long-term solutions. For the near term, the objective would be to reduce the number of tapes requiring examination and to increase the effectiveness of the forensic examiners and insure their competence and objectivity. The goal of the long-term solution would be to make it easy to authenticate tapes and, conversely, difficult to falsify them. By so doing, the time, cost, and expertise required to authenticate a tape would be reduced. The suggestions that follow are recommended steps toward solutions that will achieve these objectives.

1. Suggestions for Near-Term Solutions

A set of procedures should be drawn up for use by the technical personnel who check, install, and control equipment and tapes before, during, and after the making of a recording. The procedures should be designed to minimize the likelihood of accident or of innocuously generated signs suggestive of falsification, and to increase the information available to a forensic examiner. The list of procedures should be composed by an experienced forensic examiner working in conjunction with or in consultation with a colleague and with several experienced technical personnel drawn from major police forces and Government investigative agencies.

If at all possible, the equipment that was used in the recording of tapes should be sealed along with the tapes. If this is not possible, the equipment should be provided to the court at the time the tapes are submitted for sealing, for the purpose of making test recordings that will characterize the recording system. These should be made by or under the supervision of a qualified expert and the resulting test tape sealed together with the tapes that are to be offered into evidence.

A set of specifications should be developed to aid courts, prosecutors, and defense attorneys in evaluating the qualifications of parties who might be called upon to perform forensic examinations of tapes. These specifications should cover areas such as academic background, experience, special skills, familiarity with necessary techniques, and access to necessary analysis equipment. The specifications should be drawn up by two experienced forensic examiners and reviewed by at least two others.

To insure maximum objectivity of the forensic examiner, he should be given only the information that is specifically needed to perform his analyses. This information concerns the equipment that was used, the manner of its use, and the characteristics of the place or places at which the recorded conversations occurred. Information on the nature of the charge or of the parties involved, or corroborative evidence relating to any aspect of the case should be withheld to the extent possible.

2. Suggestions for Long-Term Solutions

An ideal long-term solution to the problem of tape-authentication would be to develop a method of recording tapes that is tamper-proof. Such a method might include the use of sealed and numbered tape cartridges that are issued by a court and that are intrinsically protected against splicing and re-recording. However, tapes must be capable of being played back to be useful, and during playback they can be copied and the copies can be altered. Records of the serial numbers of the tapes that were issued can be changed or lost, thereby permitting a forged recording to be made on court-issued tape. Some added protection would be gained if the tapes were designed to be played only on special machines and if these machines were provided only to courts. But a way still might be found to play the tapes on other machines or to gain illicit access to the special ones. Based on these and other considerations, it appears to be impossible to prevent tampering with tapes.

A practical long-term solution to the authentication problem would be to devise a method of recording that would make tampering both difficult to perform and easy to detect. This requires the development of a method of recording that will make it possible to determine easily and reliably if the exhibit tape is the original tape and if the exhibit recording is the original recording. At the same time, the technique should make it extremely difficult for a forger to falsify a tape without leaving unambiguous signs that the tape had been altered. The approach described below provides the basis

for just such a recording system.

The heart of the recording scheme is a method for permanently imbedding selected data into the recorded material in a way that is virtually undetectable during playback of the tape without the use of special-purpose equipment. Four items of data would be imbedded during each instant of the recording. These are the strength of the recorded sounds, the time elapsed during the recording, the speed of the tape, and the serial number of the tape. To provide a basis for later comparison with the imbedded data, the serial number and the distance along the tape would be permanently printed onto the tape at closely spaced intervals.

The imbedding of the sound-level, elapsed-time, and tape-speed data would be performed automatically by use of special circuitry in or attached to the original tape recorder. Serial number data could be set manually by the operator of the recording equipment and imbedded by the same circuitry.

To test a tape, the forensic examiner would play it back on special-purpose equipment that would extract the imbedded data. To determine if the exhibit tape is the original tape he would compare the serial number extracted from it with the number printed on it. A difference between these numbers would be an absolute indication that the tape was a copy. To determine if the recording had been partially erased or re-recorded he would compare the strength of the recorded materials as measured during playback with the corresponding extracted data. Electronic splicing or rearrangement of portions of the recording could be detected by testing the continuity of the extracted elapsed-time data and tape-speed data. As a final check, the distance along the tape could be computed from the elapsed-time and tape-speed data and compared with the distance printed onto the tape.

All of the above tests could be performed quickly, economically, and automatically by use of special-purpose analysis equipment that could be operated by suitably trained technicians. Thus, this approach, or one similar to it, would eliminate the need for highly-skilled personnel to perform forensic examinations of tapes. Moreover, it would make it feasible to authenticate all tapes as a matter of course at the time they are submitted to the court for sealing and, if necessary, again at the time they are offered into evidence.

APPENDIX 1—GLOSSARY OF TERMS

ACOUSTIC SOURCES Generators of sounds heard at the location of the original signal transducer. There are two types of acoustic sources: those that emanate unwanted information and noise (e.g., an extraneous talker, and background music system), and those that emanate desired information (e.g., a primary talker).

AUTHENTICATE A procedure, usually a forensic examination, that seeks to determine whether a tape was made in the manner claimed by the parties who offer it into evidence.

DELETION The physical removal of a segment of a tape or the destruction of a portion of a recording.

ELECTRICAL SIGNAL The electrical equivalent of the source signal.

EQUIPMENT SOUND A sound that can occur during the making of a recording and that arises from the operation of the equipment.

EXAMINER'S ANALYSIS EQUIPMENT Instruments used by a forensic examiner for studying the exhibit tape and the characteristics of the playback signal.

EXAMINER'S SIGNAL TRANSDUCER The device used by a forensic examiner to convert the playback signal into sound.

EXAMINER'S TAPE REPRODUCER The machine used by a forensic examiner to play back the exhibit recording.

EXHIBIT RECORDING The magnetic information that is written on the exhibit tape.

EXHIBIT TAPE The physical tape that is submitted to the forensic examiner.

EXTRANEOUS TALKER A person who, as perceived from playback of a recording, appears to have been as close to the microphone as the primary talkers.

EXTRANEOUS VOICE The voice of an extraneous talker.

FADE A substantial reduction in the strength of the recorded material.

FALSIFICATION The deliberate alteration of a tape so as to change either the audibility or the meaning of the recorded material.

FORGER'S MIXER A device used by a forger to blend the output of the forger's tape reproducer and the output of the forger's noise generator.

FORGER'S NOISE GENERATOR A device used by a forger to obscure parts of the original recording.

FORGER'S TAPE RECORDER A machine used by a forger to record the output of the forger's mixer. It can, in fact, be the original tape recorder.

FORGER'S TAPE REPRODUCER A machine used by a forger to play back the original recording.

FLUTTER The frequency modulation of tones that are present in the record signal. The modulation is caused by eccentricities of rotating parts in the tape recorder.

GAP A segment of a recording in which the character of the recorded material changes for no apparent reason.

INFORMATION INCONSISTENCY A condition that exists when the content of a recording differs from the statements, sounds, or events recalled by one of the subject talkers.

INNOCUOUS MECHANISM An undesired, naturally occurring event or condition that may affect a tape or its perceptual interpretation.

MAGNETIC DEVELOPMENT A technique for making visible the magnetic track written onto a tape by immersing the tape into a volatile fluid that contains magnetic particles in suspension and then removing the tape and allowing the fluid to evaporate.

MAGNETIC MARKS Patterns written onto a tape whenever a tape recorder is started in the record mode or stopped while in the record mode.

MAGNETIC TRACK A strip of magnetization, written onto a tape by a recorder. The width of a magnetic track usually is approximately one-quarter, one-half, or the entire width of the tape.

OBSCURATION The weakening or distorting of recorded material with the objective of making all or a part of the recording unintelligible.

ORIGINAL INTERVENING EQUIPMENT Electronic equipment that processes the electrical signal produced by the original signal transducer.

ORIGINAL RECORDING The magnetic information written on the original tape by the original tape recorder.

ORIGINAL SIGNAL TRANSDUCER The electromechanical device that is used to convert the source signal into an equivalent electrical signal.

ORIGINAL TAPE The physical tape that was used with the original tape recorder.

ORIGINAL TAPE RECORDER The machine that was used to capture and preserve the record signal.

PLAYBACK SIGNAL The electrical signal output of the examiner's tape reproducer.

PRINCIPAL TALKER A party whose speech is intended to be recorded.

POSSIBLE FALSIFICATION EQUIPMENT A variety of tools available to a forger that can be used to falsify the original recording.

RECORD SIGNAL The electrical signal after it has been processed by the original intervening equipment.

SIGNS SUGGESTIVE OF FALSIFICATION Unusual or unexpected sounds that are present during the playback of a tape, or expected sounds that are absent.

SOURCE SIGNAL The combined sound output of the acoustic sources in the environment of the original signal transducer.

SYNTHESIS The generation of a recording that is wholly artificial.

TRANSFORMATION The changing or rearranging of portions of a recording so as to alter the meaning of the recorded material.

TRANSIENT An abrupt sound of short duration (such as a click, pop, or thump) that usually lasts less that one-tenth of a second and frequently less than one-hundredth of a second.

YOU WILL ALSO WANT TO READ:

☐ **58075 SATELLITE SURVEILLANCE,** *by Harold Hough.* Once the exclusive tool of governments, satellite technology is now available to anyone. Using actual satellite photos, *Satellite Surveillance* shows you where to buy satellite images, how to enhance and interpret them, and how to hide from "the eye in the sky." This book is an essential reference for anyone concerned with the uses and abuses of satellite technology. *1991, 5½ x 8½, 192 pp, illustrated, full color photos, soft cover.* **$21.95.**

☐ **55082 A PRACTICAL GUIDE TO PHOTOGRAPHIC INTELLIGENCE,** *by Harold Hough.* A guide to taking and interpreting surveillance photographs. Learn how to: Take useful photos of objects miles away, and determine their dimensions; Read documents burned to an ash; Take aerial photographs; Use infrared light to compare invisible images; Develop film anywhere, anytime; Legally use surveillance photographs for commercial purposes; And much more. Includes actual spy photographs and many helpful illustrations. *1990, 5½ x 8½, 136 pp, illustrated, soft cover.* **$14.95.**

☐ **55090 BE YOUR OWN DICK, Private Investigating Made Easy,** *by John Q. Newman.* Most detective work involves simple research you can do for yourself — if you know where to look. This book will teach you how to find out *everything* about your target's finances, health, employment, pastimes, and "past lives." If you want to know whether they're on the level or a fraud, whether they're cheating on you, stealing from you, or lying to you, then **Be Your Own Dick.** *1992, 5½ x 8½, 113 pp, soft cover.* **$12.00.**

☐ **91085 SECRETS OF A SUPER HACKER,** *by The Knightmare, with the Introduction by Gareth Branwyn.* The most amazing book on computer hacking ever written! Step-by-step, illustrated details on the techniques used by hackers to get at your data including: Guessing Passwords; Stealing Passwords; Passwords Lists; Social Engineering; Reverse Social Engineering; Crashing Electronic Bulletin Boards; Dummy Screens; Trap Doors; And much more! The how-to text is highlighted with bare knuckle tales of the Knightmare's hacks. No person concerned with computer security should miss this amazing manual on mayhem. *1994, 8½ x 11, 205 pp, illustrated, soft cover.* **$19.95**

☐ **10052 CODE MAKING AND CODE BREAKING,** *by Jack Luger.* We live in an information age: information is bought, sold and stolen like any other good. Businesses and individuals are learning to keep their secrets safe with this practical illustrated guide to building and busting codes. Learn how computers are used to make and break codes. Learn why the most unbreakable code isn't always the best. Ideal for those interested in professional and personal privacy. *1990, 5½ x 8½, 125 pp, illustrated, soft cover.* **$10.95.**

Be sure and see our catalog ad on the next page. We carry the very best in controversial and unusual books found anywhere. If you place an order for any of the books on this page you will receive the catalog Free.

◆ ◆

LOOMPANICS UNLIMITED   **WT95**
PO Box 1197
Port Townsend, WA 98368

Please send me the books I have checked above. I have enclosed $_____ plus $4.00 shipping and handling for 1 to 3 books, or $6.00 for 4 or more. Washington residents please include 7.9% sales tax.

Name_____

Address_____

City/State/Zip_____

We now accept MasterCard and Visa. To place credit card orders only,
call 1-800-380-2230, 9am to 4pm, PST, Monday thru Friday.

"Yes, there are books about the skills of apocalypse — spying, surveillance, fraud, wiretapping, smuggling, self-defense, lockpicking, gunmanship, eavesdropping, car chasing, civil warfare, surviving jail, and dropping out of sight. Apparently writing books is the way mercenaries bring in spare cash between wars. The books are useful, and it's good the information is freely available (and they definitely inspire interesting dreams), but their advice should be taken with a salt shaker or two and all your wits. A few of these volumes are truly scary. Loompanics is the best of the Libertarian suppliers who carry them. Though full of 'you'll-wish-you'd-read-these-when-it's-too-late' rhetoric, their catalog is genuinely informative."

— **The Next Whole Earth Catalog**

THE BEST BOOK CATALOG IN THE WORLD!!!

We offer hard-to-find books on the world's most unusual subjects. Here are a few of the topics covered IN-DEPTH in our exciting new catalog:

- *Hiding/Concealment of physical objects! A complete section of the best books ever written on hiding things.*
- *Fake ID/Alternate Identities! The most comprehensive selection of books on this little-known subject ever offered for sale! You have to see it to believe it!*
- *Investigative/Undercover methods and techniques! Professional secrets known only to a few, now revealed to you to use! Actual police manuals on shadowing and surveillance!*
- *And much, much more, including Locks and Locksmithing, Self-Defense, Intelligence Increase, Life Extension, Money-Making Opportunities, Human Oddities, Exotic Weapons, Sex, Drugs, Anarchism, and more!*

Our book catalog is 292 pages, 8½ x 11, packed with over 800 of the most controversial and unusual books ever printed! You can order every book listed! Periodic supplements keep you posted on the LATEST titles available!!! Our catalog is $5.00, including shipping and handling.

Our book catalog is truly THE BEST BOOK CATALOG IN THE WORLD! Order yours today. You will be very pleased, we know.

LOOMPANICS UNLIMITED
PO BOX 1197
PORT TOWNSEND, WA 98368
USA
Now accepting Visa and MasterCard. 1-800-380-2230 for credit card orders *only.*
Office Hours: 9am to 4pm, PST, Monday thru Friday.